THE GALLIFREY CHRONICLES

THE GALLIFREY CHRONICLES

by John Peel

First published in Great Britain in 1991 by
Doctor Who Books
An imprint of Virgin Publishing
338 Ladbroke Grove
London W10 5AH

Copyright © John Peel 1991
Doctor Who copyright
© British Broadcasting Corporation 1991

Photographic illustrations
© BBC Photography Library
Additional Material Supplied by
David J. Howe & Stephen James Walker

Cover illustration by Andrew Skilleter

Additional illustrations by Trevor Baxendale

This book is published by arrangement with
BBC Books, a division of BBC Enterprises Ltd.
Doctor Who is a registered trade mark of
The British Broadcasting Corporation

Designed and typeset by
Mark Stammers
D&S Design Partnership,
1 Edith Grove, London SW10 0JY

Printed and bound by
Singapore National
Printers

ISBN 1 852 273271

CONTENTS

	Introduction	**1**
Chapter 1:	**Gallifrey**	**5**
Chapter 2:	**The Physical Nature of the Time Lords**	**11**
Chapter 3:	**Temporal Engineering**	**19**
Chapter 4:	**The Matrix**	**23**
Chapter 5:	**Politics**	**27**
Chapter 6:	**The Doctor and the Time Lords**	**33**
Chapter 7:	**Susan**	**39**
Chapter 8:	**Romana**	**43**
Chapter 9:	**Rassilon**	**47**
Chapter 10:	**Omega**	**51**
Chapter 11:	**The Monk**	**57**
Chapter 12:	**The Master**	**59**
Chapter 13:	**Borusa**	**73**
Chapter 14:	**The Rani**	**77**
Chapter 15:	**The Valeyard**	**81**
Chapter 16:	**The Guardians**	**87**
Chapter 17:	**The Renegades**	**91**
Chapter 18:	**Other Time Lords**	**97**
Appendix I:	**The Scrolls of Rassilon**	**105**
Appendix II:	**The Cast List**	**135**

This is for Jean-Marc and Randy Lofficier,
for both their friendship and their help.

INTRODUCTION

When *Doctor Who* began in 1963, we knew very little indeed about the main character of the series – hence the question-like title for the show. He was a mysterious old man who travelled in time and space in a futuristic device known as the TARDIS, but which looked (at least externally) like a police telephone call box familiar in the England of 1963. His initial companion was a young girl, Susan Foreman, who called him 'grandfather'. Beyond that, we were told very little. It became quickly apparent that he had little control over the TARDIS, and that he was in no hurry to go anywhere or anywhen in particular.

In 1963, when Verity Lambert and David Whitaker – producer and story editor respectively of the new series – were planning *Doctor Who*, their initial ideas were very different from what eventually became accepted. Writer Anthony Coburn produced a series of drafts for what was to become the first story, *The Tribe of Gum*. One version of the first episode of this story (*An Unearthly Child*) was sent out to other prospective writers for the show to introduce them to the style of the stories and the characters with whom they would have to deal. A revised version of this script was then filmed as the pilot for the programme.

The clues about Susan's background are laid out, one by one. Ian Chesterton, her science teacher, set the class a problem in orbital calculation. Susan's response was not what he expected. 'She said she wasn't interested in the conquest of mere distance. That learning how to travel a long way . . . outer space or anywhere . . . was scientifically short-sighted . . . I said: "What do you want to do, Miss Foreman? Break through to the Fourth Dimension?" That's space and time. She went as white as a sheet. As though I'd insulted her. Really white. And trembling.' Ian and his companion, Barbara Wright, followed Susan 'home' to the junkyard of 76 Totter's Lane.

The first Doctor unlocking the TARDIS door (*Marco Polo*).

Stumbling inside the TARDIS, they found Susan and her mysterious grandfather. She explained: 'I made up "TARDIS" from the initials. Time And Relative Dimension In Space. I thought you'd both realize where you were when you saw the different space the inside has from its outward appearance.' The Doctor then added: 'We are not of this race. We are not of this Earth. We are wanderers in the fourth dimension of space and time, cut off from our own planet and our own people by aeons and universes that are beyond the reach of your most advanced sciences.' Susan then revealed that she was born in the 49th century. Unable to believe this, Ian called the quest for time travel 'a scientific dream that I don't expect to find resolved in a junkyard.'

'A dream for your science, schoolteacher, not for ours,' the Doctor retorted. 'I tell you that before your ancestors had turned the first wheel the people of my world had reduced movement through the farthest reaches of space to a game for children.'

I had the opportunity to talk with Carole Ann Ford, who played Susan Foreman, on the occasion of her first Convention appearance, and I asked her if the original cast had been told anything at all about the Doctor's background. She replied that this had not been dealt with in detail, but that the idea had been that some terrible catastrophe had affected their home planet, and the Doctor and Susan had escaped it only by taking the TARDIS and fleeing. They wanted to return home, but did not know how to get back, or if it would be safe to return. None of this was ever stated on the screen, and it was later dropped in favour of a different explanation of the Doctor's origin. But in 1963, the viewers knew none of this.

Things changed very little over the course of the next few years, and even though we were to witness the Doctor's amazing ability to regenerate – from William Hartnell to Patrick Troughton – in 1966, we discovered no more about the Doctor's background until the final Patrick Troughton story, *The War Games*. At last, we met the Doctor's own people, the Time Lords, and discovered why he had left them. We also visited their home world, which was not named, even though we saw only a courtroom and a TARDIS docking bay.

With the appearance of Jon Pertwee in the role of the Doctor, the Time Lords began to take a progressively larger stance in the stories – even if only relatively. It was not until the end of 1973, in the story *The Time Warrior*, that we first learned the name of the planet where the Time Lords lived – Gallifrey. As Tom Baker took over the role, we had the first story fully set on Gallifrey (*The Deadly Assassin*) and the Doctor even took on Romana, another Time Lord, as his companion. Since that time, the other incarnations of the Doctor – Peter Davison, Colin Baker and Sylvester McCoy – have all faced adventures involving others of his race.

These tales have all offered us small segments of information about the Time Lords – their history, their origins, the details of their daily lives. The purpose of this book is to organize the information given over the course of all of the series into coherent chapters that deal with the different aspects of the Time Lords. I have also taken the liberty of speculating how what we know fits together, or how some facts – not explained in the series – may have come about. Such sections containing my theories are clearly marked, to distinguish them from the facts offered us in the television stories themselves.

All of the televised stories have provided the information used here on the Time Lords. I should point out, though, that there are certain sources of information that have not been followed. The never-shown story *Shada* has not been used, even though it did deal with the Time Lords. Since it was never finished or transmitted, I have elected to ignore it in these pages. I have also ignored (or downplayed, at the very least) other written sources of information about the Time Lords, such as those contained in the Target novelizations of the television stories. This is not to slight the books or their authors, but my ground rule for compiling this volume has always been to use only the information we have been given in the television stories. There is enough confusion from time to time in those without the need to introduce further possibilities by adding anything mentioned in the books!

Specifically in this category, I have ignored Eric Saward's *Birth of a Renegade* short story offered us in the *Radio Times 20th Anniversary Special*. The story of the Doctor's and the Master's origin he gave us there seems to me to be completely at variance with what we have been told in the series.

There has been very little effort on my part to compile a 'history' of the sort that will give dates and specifics on Time Lord history. This is for two reasons. Firstly, we have never been given any absolute dates for any of the Time Lord stories, or the details about their past. Secondly, dates become meaning-

The seventh incarnation of the Doctor.

Ian, Barbara and Susan returning to the TARDIS at the end of their first adventure (*The Tribe of Gum*).

less for any race that dwells – as the Time Lords do – outside Time itself. Any attempt to be specific about when a given story takes place is doomed to failure. The Doctor himself interacts with the Time Lords over a vast stretch of time. He may have aged only 200 years during the course of his televised adventures, but it seems that for the Time Lords several millennia have passed between *The War Games* and *The Trial of a Time Lord*. Any attempt to pinpoint dates, therefore, must end up as pure speculation.

Nor is this volume an attempt to survey the various theories about the Time Lords that have appeared over the years. Are they the all-powerful figures they seem to be in *The War Games*, or are they more like the run-down old men we were shown in *The Deadly Assassin*? Again, such speculation is a trifle pointless, since over the course of the millennia the Time Lords have undoubtedly been both. As the Doctor tried to explain to the Sisterhood of Karn in *The Brain of Morbius*, with death comes change. Since Time Lords rarely die, they clearly just as rarely change. Inertia, stagnation and decay become the order of the day until swept clean as fresher minds gain political control of Gallifrey.

I have tried as best I can to meld into a unified whole all of the information on the Time Lords given over the twenty-seven years of *Doctor Who*'s existence, without giving in to any desire to criticize any stories or facts that may have seemed to me to be difficult to accept – or even downright silly. You will not find in these pages any opinions about the contents, writing or filming of the stories. What follows is purely an attempt to gather together the facts about the Time Lords – individually and collectively – given to us. The interpretation of these facts is purely my own, and all readers should feel free to cheerfully disregard any of my theories that they don't like. Hopefully, though, my speculations will make a certain amount of sense to you all.

Finally, I must offer my thanks to various people who have offered information or advice (which I may or may not have taken!) in the preparation of this volume. As ever, I am very grateful to Jeremy and Paula Bentham for all their help. Many thanks to my agent, Mary Jack Wald, for her help in all of my projects. Also to Terry Nation for his help in formulating the portions relating to the earliest days of the series. And to Peter Darvill-Evans, the editor of the *Doctor Who* imprint, for his encouragement and help. To John Nathan-Turner, who helped with certain details about the stories. And finally to my wife, Nan, for sitting and listening to me expounding on my ideas, and yet still remaining sane!

CHAPTER 1:

GALLIFREY

Gallifrey lies some 29,000 light years from the Earth, according to the unnamed Time Lord in *Terror of The Autons*. It is in the neighbourhood of Karn (*The Brain of Morbius*) and the Five Planets. Our Galaxy is approximately 100,000 light years in diameter, so Gallifrey is clearly well within our own Galaxy, but a considerable distance from the Earth. It is almost certainly not in the spiral arm that contains the Earth, and is most likely closer to the Galactic centre than the Earth. (The centre of our Galaxy is about 30,000 light years from the Earth, but astronomers theorize that it may be the site of a gigantic black hole – in which case, it is unlikely that Gallifrey lies too close to it. An intriguing speculation is that the black hole might be the one created by the Time Lord known as Omega...)

Susan, the Doctor's granddaughter, talked about her home world to the Sensorites. 'Grandfather and I don't come from Earth,' she informed the First Elder. 'Oh, it's *ages* since we've seen our planet. It's quite like Earth... But at night the sky is a burned orange. And the leaves on the trees are bright silver!' The orange sky is clearly formed because the atmosphere on Gallifrey is thinner than that of the Earth, and was actually seen in *The Invasion of Time* when Leela left the Citadel. This thinner atmosphere would

The Panopticon, the political centre of Gallifrey. *Inset*: In the Panopticon - the Presidential resignation from *The Deadly Assassin.*

Earth did in its earliest days in the form of heat and radiation from both its sun and perhaps from nearby stars. This could have accelerated the evolutionary process and resulted in the formation of humanoid life on Gallifrey before any comparable life existed elsewhere in the Galaxy. It could also have caused the atmospheric thinning, the extra heat driving the gases off into space faster than has happened on the Earth.

We know nothing of these earlier inhabitants of Gallifrey, whose past is shrouded in the mysteries of vast gulfs of time. They probably went through many of the wars, periods of progress and periods of regress that we humans have faced. Certainly, their temperaments seem to be very like our own. They are capable of love, hate, compassion, fury, greed, self-sacrifice and other emotions, and their earliest days must have evidenced this. They progressed through civilization after civilization until they reached the plateau of technology. Here, for a while, they rested.

In *The War Games*, the Doctor tells Jamie and Zoe that his people are the only ones with the secret of time and space travel. One reason for this is simple – they repress other attempts to travel in such dimensions (for example, they attempted to forbid Dastari's experiments in *The Two Doctors*). The Time Lords keep their knowledge of temporal control strictly to themselves.

This is not to say that they absolutely forbid other travelling in time. They apparently do not consider the Daleks to be much competition here. The Daleks used time machines to try to kill the Doctor in *The Chase* and *The Daleks' Masterplan*. But the Daleks' machines are simply examples of using brute force to smash their way between times, and do not show any true understanding of the nature of Time itself. Other time travellers have also been allowed to go their ways, but any attempts to manipulate time have been firmly quashed.

The Doctor also mentions that the Time Lords are content simply to observe events. Their passion for involvement has mostly spent itself. In *Underworld*, we are told that their policy of non-involvement came about because of the Minyans. When the Time Lords first achieved their powers, they wanted to help other worlds. About a hundred thousand years ago, they chose Minyos, a close neighbour in space, and attempted to raise their culture. Instead, they induced stresses into Minyan society that led to atomic war.

The first Doctor and Susan with two Sensorites (*The Sensorites*).

explain why Time Lords possess a refined respiratory system that can extract oxygen from even the trace of an atmosphere.

In *The Trial of a Time Lord*, the Doctor calls his own race 'the oldest civilization' in the Universe. He also mentions that they have had ten million years of absolute power – and have become absolutely corrupt. In *Genesis of the Daleks*, the Time Lord who speaks with the Doctor mentions that they passed by the use of merely mechanical devices like a Transmat 'when the Universe was less than half its present size.' The Universe is about 15 billion years old, and the Sun and other stars probably began to condense out of clouds of mostly hydrogen gas about 4.6 billion years ago. Life began on the Earth between three and a half and two and a half billion years ago. Similar figures most likely will apply to Gallifrey.

The Time Lords must have evolved faster than humans on the Earth did. If, as seems reasonably likely, Gallifrey is closer than Earth to the Galactic centre, then it received much more energy than the

Horrified at this unintended result, the Time Lords vowed never to interfere in the progress of another society again. Like many Time Lord vows, it was never terribly strictly kept.

Like many ageing societies, the Time Lords preserve the forms of the past, and are reluctant to accept change. Somewhat facetiously, the Doctor suggests that the worst punishment he could receive at their hands would be a harsh speech because 'they like making speeches'. Everything that we hear about them suggests an ancient culture, powerful but unwilling to take any action unless they are forced to do so.

The Time Lords all dwell within the boundaries of the Citadel on Gallifrey. This is an immense structure, and virtually self-sufficient. We are never told whether it is a single building or a city in its own right, but the size and variations seen within it suggest the latter. It probably began as the fortified home of the original Time Lords when they emerged from within the general population of Gallifrey. Over the passage of millennia, it must have grown to become an impressive city in its own right.

Presumably, it is not the only city on Gallifrey, but it is the one inhabited only by Time Lords and their servants. Its denizens view the rest of the planet as barren desert – which is plainly untrue, but since they rarely leave the Citadel they neither know nor care about the reality of their planet. As far as they are concerned, anything outside the boundaries of the Citadel, whether on another plant or on Gallifrey itself, is in a state of primitivism or anarchy. The Time Lords crave stability and a lack of change, and it is only within the confines of the Citadel that they can – usually – find these states of peace.

The Doctor mentions at one point (in *The Time Monster*) that he lived in a house that was halfway up a mountainside. This was situated in South Gallifrey. Clearly, then, there are plenty of other cities on Gallifrey, else why would he feel the need to specify that his home was in South Gallifrey? Presumably, such towns, homes or villages are home to the general population, or to Time Lords who have not yet confined themselves to the Citadel.

The Citadel contains the power source for the Time Lords' control of time and space, and the Matrix, their repository of all knowledge. Though most Time Lords live here, not all who live here are Time Lords. The junior grades of technicians appear to be normal beings, as do the security forces.

In *The Three Doctors*, the action on Gallifrey takes place in the Time Control Chamber. Here, the energy levels needed for time travel and time manipulation are monitored and controlled. In ultimate charge of these operations (at least at this point in time) is the President of the Council. His post is clearly shown to be of a technical nature – he understands and controls the technicians that staff the room.

Above him – theoretically at least – in the hierarchy of Time Lords was the Chancellor. This person was a politician, more concerned with regulations and appearances than with operations and work. When the renegade Time Lord Omega attacked Gallifrey, the President decided to use past incarnations of the Doctor to help the present one. The Chancellor's reaction is one of horror: the First Law of Time expressly forbids a Time Lord to meet himself. Despite this, the President pressed ahead with his plan.

The First Law is obviously a law of convenience, and not one of nature, since it can be (and was) broken quite simply. The reasons for its existence are quite clear – giving a past incarnation of a Time Lord knowledge of his own future can affect the course of the time stream. Clearly, in the case of the Doctor, this is precisely what has happened. Beginning at this point in time, the entire life-flow of the Doctor has been altered by the interference of the Time

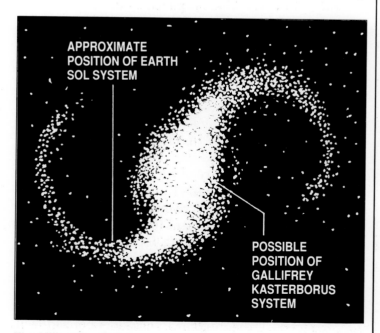

The Milky Way Galaxy.

APPROXIMATE POSITION OF EARTH SOL SYSTEM

POSSIBLE POSITION OF GALLIFREY KASTERBORUS SYSTEM

Shabogans, as seen in *The Invasion of Time*.

Lords. (For more details on this, see Chapter 6.)

The President speaks of the Time Lords protecting species weaker than themselves, and is clearly appalled at the thought that they, too, might revert to that status if Omega's attack on them should succeed. He seems more afraid of their losing their great powers than of the possibility that they might be physically wiped out. The Time Lords have held their absolute sway over Time for so long that the mere thought of losing it is enough to terrify them. We might wonder whether their concept of 'protecting' other species is understood in the same way by the other species in question. Sometimes, no doubt, the Time Lords act for the good of all. They banned the use of the Scope (*Carnival of Monsters*), for example, because it exploited the weaker races and turned them into entertainment for stronger ones. They also helped out the inhabitants of the Earth and many other worlds by sealing the Fendahleen within a time bubble (*Image of The Fendahl*). The War Lord's crime in *The War Games* is that he and his race preyed upon weaker societies to achieve their own ends.

Yet this 'protection' is very subjective. The Time Lords are quite willing to allow races as evil as the Daleks, the Cybermen, the Yeti and the Dominators to exist and act as they will, as the second Doctor pointed out in his own defence at his first trial. They took action against the Daleks only when they foresaw a time when the Daleks might be able to subjugate the entire Universe – Gallifrey, presumably, included. And often the Time Lords' interference has been merely to protect their own bastion of power, such as in strictly controlling other species' experimentations into time travel. The races that know of the Time Lords – since the Time Lords have never been particularly secretive about themselves – generally have a very low opinion of them.

The Time Lords also appear to be pretty complacent about the damage caused to other species by members of their own race. The Master, for example, is a mass murderer probably unsurpassed in all of Time and Space. Yet the Time Lords don't seem to be bothered about capturing or punishing him. When he escaped from prison on Gallifrey (*Terror of The Autons*), the most that the Time Lords did was warn the Doctor – they didn't even offer him any help. And both The Rani (*The Mark of The Rani*) and Azmael (*The Twin Dilemma*) left Gallifrey and began to rule other planets without interference from the Time Lords. Either the Time Lords were staggeringly ignorant of their actions, or else they simply didn't care. One can only wonder why they objected so vehemently to the Doctor's interference in the lives of other races. The most immediate possibility is that having helped them, the Doctor always left the inhabitants of a planet to fend for themselves. Both the Rani and Azmael simply took control of their respective worlds. The Time Lords are not opposed to control, but they do not approve of the Doctor's attempts to make other beings more self-reliant.

Significantly, the Time Lords appear to be very interested in the Earth. Not only the Doctor, but Drax, K'Anpo Rimpoche and other Time Lords have either visited or moved here. And even those who have never visited the planet have heard of it. Given that many times the Doctor has intervened in cases where humans were dealing with time travel, is it possible that the Time Lords foresee a time when the human race might become their rivals in the mastery of time and space?

The Capital is a complex of buildings. Though Time Control is the heart of the Time Lords' power, the centrepiece of the city is the Panopticon. This building is the political centre of the Time Lords' civilization. The High Council meets here, and its individual members have their offices here. So, too, does the President of the Time Lords. The Great Gallery of the Panopticon is where all ruling Time Lords, arranged by Chapters, gather.

Directly below the Panopticon Galleries and offices is Security Control, where the complex equipment powering the Transduction Barriers is housed. The Transduction Barriers were credited as one of Rassilon's inventions (for information on Rassilon and the legends that have grown up about him, see Chapter 9). The Transduction Barriers surround the entire planet of Gallifrey, and prevent any unauthorized access. While they are in place no craft, not even the Time Lords' own TT capsules, can land on the planet. A second setting, allowing access by authorized TT capsules whilst still resisting access to all other forms of craft, is possible.

When the Vardans and Sontarans invaded Gallifrey (*The Invasion of Time*), they could only do so once the Barriers had been lowered about the Citadel. However, in *The War Games* the forces of the War Lord have little difficulty in landing their SIDRATs on Gallifrey in their futile attempt to rescue him. Perhaps this was because they still had the landing codes programmed into them from the time when the War Chief stole them from Gallifrey. The Master, too, managed to land on Gallifrey undetected (*The Deadly Assassin*), though in his case he had the assistance of Goth, a high-ranking Time Lord, who might conveniently have smuggled in the Master's TARDIS. Also, Omega in *Arc of Infinity* managed to make contact with Hedin without much difficulty and without being monitored. We can only wonder whether the Transduction Barriers are quite as impregnable as the Time Lords might wish to believe they are.

Space Traffic Control is also housed within the Panopticon complex. Here, technicians monitor passing space and time craft, ensuring that none are approaching Gallifrey too closely. The job is a Seventh Grade appointment, but as Rodan, one holder of the office observed, the technician is little more than a 'glorified traffic guard'. While the Transduction Barriers hold, nothing can land without authorization on Gallifrey anyway. Obviously, then, Space Traffic Control is really simply another of the endless manifestations of the Time Lords' passion for information (however meaningless), security and caution.

Close to the Panopticon Galleries is the Conference Room, where meetings of the Inner Council are held. Behind this room, accessed only by a musical code played on the Harp of Rassilon, stands the hidden room controlling the forbidden Time Scoop. Both the President and the Chancellor have offices in this general area.

Beside the Panopticon is the Communications Tower, which stands some 53 stories high. From here, all communications with passing space and time vessels is carried out. This is also the home of Public Record Video, which tapes and transmits all events of importance from within the Citadel to the rest of Gallifrey.

The Time Lords who live in the Citadel rarely venture outside, and often appear completely unconscious (and uncaring) of what may exist in the Outer World, or Outer Gallifrey (both names are concurrent, and both suggest banishment or worse from the serenity of the Citadel). It is, for the most part, a vast wasteland. The planet was clearly once ruined by technology, but it has managed to recover now that the Time Lords have forsworn the use of crude technology. Plants, trees and wild animals all abound in the wastelands.

Some Time Lords have turned their back on their life of ease and gone outside the Citadel. The Doctor knew one such, a hermit who dwelt in a cave atop the mountain the Doctor lived on as a child. Many of these exiles have banded together to form a more primitive society. They eschew all technology beyond the simple weapons and villages that they need in order to survive. Though their existence is known at least to the High Council, it is never made public knowledge, thus avoiding the need for any explanation for their behaviour. The official line is that Outer Gallifrey is a dead, inhospitable place. To admit to the existence of a band of exiles living just outside the holy environs of the Citadel might raise some prickly questions as to why anyone should want to abandon their homes for the wilderness. To the Council, a small deception is worth the serenity it causes. For the same reason – not wishing to alarm the body of the populace, or to make them dissatisfied with their lot – knowledge of the Doctor and his initial trial was kept quiet. So were the crimes and punishment of the Master. In *The Deadly Assassin*, virtually no one – even the Castellan, in charge of security – had ever heard of either of them.

Somewhere in all the vast outer wasteland stands the Death Zone. It is ringed by a range of mountains, and surrounded by a force field. Within the Zone, the Games were once played, until banned by the decree of Rassilon. The exact location of the Death Zone is unknown to the current residents of Gallifrey, and no one would be foolish enough to want to visit it anyway. (The Doctor, who was forced to be there, in fact spoke of *returning* to Gallifrey from the Zone, as if it were somehow not physically a part of Gallifrey – an intriguing thought in itself.

The President in the Time Control Room (*The Three Doctors*).

CHAPTER 2:
THE PHYSICAL NATURE OF THE TIME LORDS

To a cursory inspection, the Time Lords look like fairly normal human beings. This belies their actual nature, as their bodies are vastly different from ours. The most obvious difference is that when the Time Lords age, or when their bodies are subjected to stresses that would kill a normal being, they have the ability to regenerate.

This regeneration takes the form of a complete physical and mental change, with their bodies and mental states both altering in a very short period of time. The changes can often be very large ones, frequently to the discomfort of people who knew the former incarnation. A regenerate Time Lord can often appear to be totally different from the person he or she may have been before. In fact, the changes are not so great as they might at first appear; there is a measure of continuity. Each regeneration is of the same basic person, but what occurs is a shift in the emphasis of the mix that makes up their physiological and psychological profiles.

The ability to regenerate is not without its limits. In *The War Games* the Doctor claims that his people 'can live forever, barring accidents'. In *The Deadly Assassin*, this is apparently modified to their having twelve regenerations only. However, in *The Five Doctors*, the Time Lords offer the Master a complete new life cycle of regenerations. In *Underworld*, the Minyans have taken basic Time Lord technology and created a machine that can regenerate their own bodies thousands of times, giving them incredibly long life spans. Since the Minyans could do this

> ### 'A man is the sum of his memories; a Time Lord even more so.'
> THE FIFTH DOCTOR, *THE FIVE DOCTORS*
>
> ### 'He's a Time Lord! In many ways, we have the same mind.'
> THE FOURTH DOCTOR, *LOGOPOLIS*

without a problem, surely the Time Lords could do no less?

How can we make sense of this? The Doctor's original claim of near-immortality is easy to understand given the sedentary nature of most Time Lords. Regeneration is generally triggered by a period of great stress, and for the vast majority of the Time Lords, such periods rarely happen. Living their quiet lives in the serenity of the Citadel, there is little danger in their lives, and few Time Lords are ready to leave the Citadel for the stresses of other places. In this environment, then, Time Lords probably do live a nearly immortal life.

Those who elect to leave the Citadel will naturally use up their regenerations faster. Time Lords like the Master, who frequently place themselves in jeopardy, get through their remaining incarnations quickly. Clearly the figure of twelve regenerations is not simply a fixed sum that cannot be exceeded. In *The Five Doctors*, Rassilon is obviously an immortal being, and does not seem even to need to undergo regeneration at all. Is he a special case, or are there other Time Lords like him?

In *Destiny of The Daleks* Romana is able to shape her regeneration, which proves to be fairly fluid for a short while. In *The War Games* the second Doctor is told he will undergo a regeneration. 'I have the right to decide what I look like!' he claims, and is shown several options, none of which he likes. Clearly, then, the process of regeneration is controllable, at least to

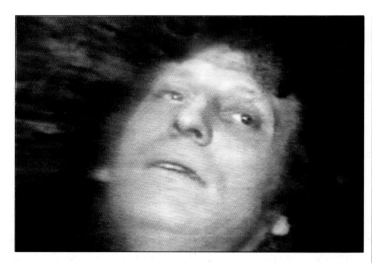

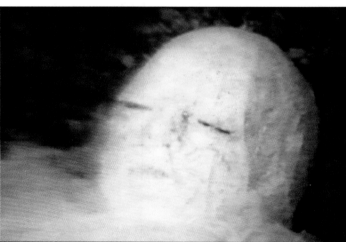

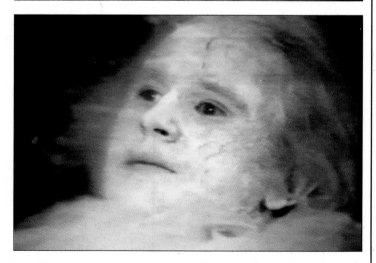

The Doctor's fourth regeneration (*Logopolis* and *Castrovalva*).

desired end result. In Romana's case, two possibilities present themselves. First, the apparent forms into which she regenerated were not true regenerations at all, but simply physical projections of potential regenerations. K'Anpo (*Planet of The Spiders*) projects his own regeneration forward in time as Choje, who can act and interact with others and with his own older self. And the Doctor even manifests one of his own, shadowy, regenerations in *Logopolis*. Alternatively, another explanation is that since this was Romana's first regeneration, the forces within her younger body made it possible to mould the shape she took as if her form were somehow 'plastic' for a while.

How does regeneration occur? In *The Twin Dilemma*, the sixth Doctor likens it to rebirth and the changing of a chrysalis into a butterfly. Certainly, on the whole, the process is very swift. The old body breaks down, and the new one takes its place – at least in the most ideal of circumstances. However, complications can arise, especially as the number of regenerations already undergone approaches the final ones permissible. In the most troublesome of cases, the Time Lords will use the Elixir Of Life to strengthen the changes (*The Brain of Morbius*). In *The Tenth Planet*, the TARDIS itself helps the ageing first Doctor to regenerate. The TARDIS is clearly mentally linked with the Doctor (see Chapter 3), and perhaps even in some way physically also. In *Planet of The Spiders* K'Anpo Rimpoche helps the dying third Doctor to regenerate by the application of his own mental energy.

Through the changes of regeneration, some measure of continuity is preserved. The Doctor, for example, undergoes any number of minor personality changes (or, at least, minor as far as he is concerned!), but the basic continuity is maintained. He retains always his sense of morality, his desire to help others, his passion for justice, and – generally – his sense of humour. However, this need not always be the case. With some Time Lords, large swings in their personalities can take place, as with Borusa (see Chapter 13). And the Valeyard is called the dark side of the Doctor, existing somewhere between his twelfth and final regeneration. Yet the Valeyard is very different from the Doctor that we know.

Along with this obvious difference of regenerative ability – which other races have envied and attempted to copy (see *Underworld* and *Mawdryn Undead* for examples), the Time Lords possess other abilities that other races do not. For example, Time

a degree. Since regeneration is an outgrowth of the Time Lord's personality, it is possible to predict future regenerations, and then (probably) possible to shape the regenerative process so as to produce the

Lords can engage in almost total metabolic shutdown in their bodies when they are faced with overwhelming assaults on their senses. It induces a state of catatonia.

Time Lords are telepathic beings, and can recognize one another using their mental patterns – highly useful since their physical appearance can change so dramatically after a regeneration. They can impart information very swiftly using mental contact. In cases like the Master, this telepathic facility is taken further and he can actually impose his own will on the mind of a weaker individual. In *The Sensorites*, Susan finds she can become much more telepathic due to the nature of the Sense-Sphere, which enhanced her natural telepathic abilities. There are times that their mental acuity is to their disadvantage, of course, as happened when Azmael was taken over mentally by the grotesque Mestor (*The Twin Dilemma*).

Time Lords have a secondary cardiovascular system that is virtually independent of their first. In the case of a heart failure in their primary system, their second heart takes over the functions of keeping the body alive while the first heart undergoes self-healing. Because of this ability to switch vital functions, Time Lords have remarkable recuperative powers. Wounds that would be fatal to normal beings can be repaired quite swiftly, and they are able to withstand tremendous strains on their systems. They are able to go into self-induced trances to draw upon this healing power.

The remarkable efficiency of their bodies has several helpful side-effects. For example, they require less sleep than other beings, as their bodies refresh themselves much more rapidly than humans could. And it is also possible for Time Lords to 'switch off' what we would consider to be essential body functions for a while. In *Terror of The Zygons*, the Doctor is able to last a period of time without breathing at all. In *Pyramids of Mars*, he avoids strangulation by means of his respiratory bypass system. In *The Hand of Fear*, gas weapons effective against Sarah seem not to affect him at all. In *Four to Doomsday*, he withstands both the vacuum and the cold of space without ill effect. In *The Armageddon Factor* the Doctor manages to survive for a short while in the mouth of a blast furnace, proving that he is almost equally impervious to short periods of intense heat.

In *The Time Monster* the Doctor mentions that his reactions are ten times faster than those of normal human beings. This is presumably because of his improved nervous system and larger brain. We are told in *Spearhead From Space* that the Doctor's normal body temperature is sixty degrees, his blood is very different from that of humans, and his heart rate is about ten beats per minute.

Time Lords have a degree of resistance to changing time fields, and are not as affected by fluctuations in space-time as other beings (as in *The Time Monster*). In *City of Death*, the Doctor showed that he possesses an awareness of changes in space and time that were undetectable by human beings. In *Meglos*, both the Doctor and Romana became aware that they were trapped within a time loop, when normal beings would never even notice such a thing (as in *Carnival of Monsters*). In *Warriors' Gate*, we are shown that Romana is a time sensitive – a weak one, but able to navigate slightly in the time streams. The Doctor has shown on occasion the ability to see into the future via his dreams (eg *The Time Monster*, *Planet of the Spiders*). It would seem that Time Lords are in some

The Watcher, the fourth Doctor's physical premonition of his impending regeneration (*Logopolis*).

way slightly dislocated from the normal laws of cause and effect, and their minds can wander – in a very small way – through time when freed in sleep.

One example of this dislocation in time is that they can materialize their own next incarnations, provided they have sufficient cause and mental resources. K'Anpo achieved this, as did the Doctor himself (*Logopolis*), though in the latter case, the projection was a subconscious and poorly formed one.

Some Speculations On Time Lord Biology

Quite clearly, Time Lords are a physically unique species. Their ability to regenerate, their secondary circulatory system and their telepathic abilities add up to an impressive total. How could this combination have come about?

I would hazard a guess that we can rule out any natural causes. As mentioned in Chapter 1, the Time Lords are the oldest species in the galaxy, and were thus the first to have evolved to intelligence. The chances that they should not only have evolved intelligence but all of the other factors as well in so short a period of time seems a trifle hard to accept. There is, to best of our knowledge, no other known example of their abilities. Some primitive organisms can undergo a measure of regrowth, but none has the ability to regenerate. No other species, not even the most primitive of life-forms, has a secondary circulatory system. And though there have been many attempts to document it, there are no accepted proven cases of telepathic manifestations. In short, there is no other case for a species having evolved even one of the Time Lords' three most remarkable attributes.

This seriously raises the possibility of their being artificially induced. At first thought, this might seem peculiar, but it isn't as far-fetched as it might sound. We know, for example, that not all the inhabitants of Gallifrey are Time Lords. The Chancellery Guards and many of the technical staff refer to the Time Lords as though they are not themselves Time Lords. It may be simply that 'Lord' here means rank, but it is most likely that while all Time Lords are Gallifreyans, not all Gallifreyans are Time Lords. It would be most reasonable if the differentiator here was the possession of the three abilities of regeneration, telepathy and dual circulatory system.

Readers of science fiction – and in some cases of science fact – may be aware of a very theoretical concept known as nanotechnology. *Nanotechnology is the concept of building machines so small that they* compete in size with naturally occurring microbes or viruses. It is, if you like, the idea of taking miniaturization to its ultimate degree – building sophisticated machines the size of microns. You may wonder why such machines would be wanted (just imagine dropping a virus-sized machine – it would be far worse than looking for a lost contact lens or the smallest needle in a planet-sized haystack!). The answer is that with nanotechnology, it becomes possible to enter the final frontier. Not space, but the cells of a living body.

We do not yet know exactly what causes cancer, but it is clear that the natural reproductive centres of the body somehow misread the genetic code that we all contain within ourselves. Instead of forming a healthy cell to replace a dead one, a wrong cell, a cancer cell, is formed instead. Since a cancer cell is a mistake, it does not work with the body, but against it, and eventually it kills. One of the problems we face with attempting to cure cancer is that there are literally millions of potential variations on the 'wrong cell' format, and we cannot evolve a single cure for them all.

This is where nanotechnology comes in. Imagine the nanomachine, if you like, as a tiny, semi-intelligent submarine. It's been equipped with two things: a map of the body's genetic pattern (each of us has a different and unique one) and a laser. The task of the little sub is to go through the body, scanning the cells it comes across. Those that conform to the genetic map it ignores. Those that vary from it (cancer cells or invading diseases) it fries on the spot.

Death to cancers – and to diseases, right down to the common cold.

Well, Time Lords are a very healthy race . . .

Of course, the nanomachines don't have to be mechanical – they could be biological, like some form of benign virus. In which case you might say that we'd become infected with health.

Take this one step further. Why do we die? Okay, let's ignore, for a moment, such obvious causes as bullets, being hit by cars or falling off cliffs. Even if we stayed home all our lives, and avoided bullets, cars and cliffs, sooner or later we'd drop dead. One reason is cancers – but with nanotechnology they can be stopped – and other diseases. And, if we applied the same technology, hereditary problems, too. (An offshoot of the same problem as cancers – the reproductive cells duplicating themselves incorrectly. The little nanosubs could fix those, too.) Still, even with all of those problems solved, we still age.

One cause of that is that some of our cells are literally irreplaceable. According to the best scientific minds, brain cells die out daily, and are never replaced. If we could live for ever, presumably we'd do so as vegetables after our brains rot out within us. But – and you're probably ahead of me here – does this have to happen? It's because sooner or later our bodies have problems replacing good cells and replace them with near-miss copies instead. That's why our skin dries out and wrinkles. Or our hair goes gray or falls out. The body eventually becomes unable to replace the dead or dying cells, and we undergo massive systems failure . . .

But do we have to? Think back to those nanomachines. What if, instead of zapping all those wrongly-made cells, they simply correct them instead? A little microsurgery, as it were? Then, suddenly, there's no real ageing, and the brain cells might be replaceable.

We might, as you've probably guessed, be able to live for ever. Can it actually be done? Well, we really don't know. Certainly not yet, at any rate. But eventually...? And maybe the Time Lords have already done this?

For the sake of argument, let's assume that the Time Lords have done something like this, and that within their bodies they have an artificial virus that renews their cells. It certainly would explain why they live longer than us. But can it explain their other advantages?

Yes.

Take, for a start, the double circulatory system. If you or I were designing a machine (for any purpose you might like) that had to be independent, would you design it so that if a single part failed, the whole machine would just die? Probably not – you'd add, say, a back-up power-pack, in case it ran out of fuel. Back

Nanomachines maintaining the status of a Time Lord's body at a microscopic level.

to our nanosubs. If they are going to force the cells within your body to conform to your genetic pattern, why not go a little further? Why not redesign that genetic pattern slightly? For example, add a second heart? After all, heart failure is a major cause of death. A secondary heart to take over in case of failure of the first would certainly save a vast number of lives. And how about adding telepathic ability? That could come in handy, too.

But – and you're probably ahead of me here, too – that would involve changing the original body, wouldn't it? After all, there's no way simply to add a second circulatory system to our existing bodies. It would be too complicated a process.

What if, though, it was simply a part of a greater change – like total bodily regeneration, for example? At the moment of change, the original genetic material would be acted upon virtually instantaneously by the nanodevices, which would then restructure the body in its new configuration. Two hearts, for example, and other changes. Probably tidy up the physical features a bit, knock a few years off the appearance, and so forth. It might even cause a few side-effects, such as personality changes . . .

In short, you have bodily regeneration. Exactly what a Time Lord undergoes.

Is there any proof that something like this in fact occurs? Not much, sadly, but there is a little. The first incarnation of the Doctor was not quite like his other incarnations. Aside from his vast age, he apparently had a few other physical differences. He slept normal hours, for example. And, in The Sensorites, *when the Doctor is injured, Ian Chesterton reports that his heart is beating normally. Not hearts. Perhaps, at that time, he had only the one, and it wasn't until he regenerated that his secondary circulatory system was developed. Also the first Doctor didn't seem to be telepathic, unlike all of his later selves . . .*

Intriguing, isn't it?

Let's take these ideas a few steps further. Perhaps these nanomachines can explain a few more things. Why are there only a few Time Lords? Why aren't all Gallifreyans Time Lords? Back once again to the idea of being 'infected' by the nanodevices. Any such device would be a tremendously complex creation. It might well not be able to work on everyone. There would be bound to be people whose bodies resisted the changes (or to whom they might even prove fatal). What if only a small percentage of Gallifreyans were naturally able to accept the nanomachines that could help them to regenerate? Thus the precondition for a Gallifreyan becoming a Time Lord wouldn't be one of ability or suitability (after all, look at some of the beings who are Time Lords! Who would have chosen them?). It comes down instead to simply whether or not the nanosubs can work their healing ways within you.

That would certainly explain why there are so few Time Lords. It would also explain a few other matters.

For example, though Susan is the Doctor's grand-daughter, we never do hear of the Doctor having any other relatives. Well, if the ability to co-exist with the nanodevices was the criterion for immortality, then you wouldn't – the Doctor's children would have been non-compatible, and be long since dead. Only Susan from his immediate family would have been Time Lord material.

Another thing the nanodevices could explain is the 'twelve regenerations' rule. The initial injection (or whatever) that infected the neophyte Time Lord with the devices would be good for twelve uses. Then the devices themselves would need regenerating. Now, the rule given the Time Lords would seem to be that each Time Lord gets one shot, as it were, at immortality, and after twelve regenerations, that's it. Yet, as we have seen, in The Five Doctors, *the High Council offers the Master a whole new regenerative cycle. What do they know that we don't? Maybe that the Master could have a second shot of the nanomachines? And that they would continue to be effective within his new body? So Time Lords might be able to go on beyond their allotted span of twelve regenerations.*

And take the case of Rassilon. He doesn't seem to have died after he must have used up all of his twelve (see Chapter 9). Did he undergo a different sort of infection, one without the limit of twelve regenerations? Or one in which it became unnecessary to undergo regeneration?

In The Five Doctors, *Borusa sought the immortality promised by Rassilon. Borusa was a bright man, even if ultimately corrupted. Something must have given him reason to believe that Rassilon had the power to bestow the immortality promised on him. Perhaps the Black Scrolls of Rassilon contained information about a second, more powerful, strain of nanodevices?*

As to how the Time Lords could either control or predict – at least initially – their future incarnations, it would seem to be a combination of two factors. First, they do seem to be slightly able to dislocate themselves from the time stream. In this case, they could 'view' their possible incarnations, and select the behaviour that would lead them to one and not to another. Secondly, there is within their genetic structure a certain stability that should make predictable the possible permutations open to them. It then only becomes necessary to instruct the nanodevices to select the desired form and trigger the regeneration.

Lord President Borusa, who plotted to share Rassilon's secret of eternal life (*The Five Doctors*).

When the first Doctor regenerated, he needed the help of the TARDIS to do so. The TARDIS could have provided the necessary information to the devices to guide the regeneration. In the case of the regeneration of the second Doctor, the Time Lord Tribunal itself triggered the regeneration and decided on his final appearance. When the third Doctor regenerated, it was K'Anpo/Cho-je who started the process. The regenerations of the fourth, fifth and sixth Doctors were all managed under dire stress (the regenerations of the latter two taking place within the TARDIS, which may have helped), and all three caused more than normal regenerative problems. Given the lack of input on all three of his latest incarnations, it is small wonder that he appeared frequently to be a trifle unstable in them.

The business of regeneration has some interesting social ramifications, which tend to bear out what we have been shown in the series. First of all, Time Lords do not appear to marry. We have never been shown any family of a Time Lord, other than the case of Susan, the Doctor's granddaughter. None of the Time Lords we have encountered seem to be married, or to have anything resembling a family life. True, Andred married Leela in The Invasion Of Time, but Andred was not a Time Lord – he was a Gallifreyan. And Susan married David Campbell in The Dalek Invasion Of Earth, but this was in the context of Earth relationships, not Gallifreyan ones. And, besides this, we do not know for certain that Susan was indeed a Time Lord. She could have been simply a Gallifreyan, lacking the ability to regenerate.

The reason for this lack of family and spouses is quite obvious, given the nature of regeneration. If the person you were married to might regenerate tomorrow into someone totally different, it is more than likely that you'd have a hard time electing to stay married to them. Since both physical and psychological changes occur with regeneration, it seems reasonable to suggest that the only Time Lords who marry are likely to be those who have not yet undergone their first regeneration. Thereafter, the formation of long-term relationships would be precluded.

This also explains why few Time Lords seem to have long-term friendships. True, the Doctor views Hedin as his friend (in Arc Of Infinity), but Hedin betrays the Doctor. Again, the problems of maintaining continuity of relationships across the boundaries between regenerations seems to be difficult. It is not, however,

impossible – the Doctor himself has proven that. But by any standards, the Doctor is no ordinary Time Lord anyway.

Secondly, the Time Lords seem to have a very low libido and an abnormally low interest in sex. This again is understandable because of the faculty of regeneration. The evolution of sex and sexual drives is a biological necessity to preserve the species. Most animals and humans have a relatively short life-expectancy, and the only way to survive as a species is by breeding as often as possible. In nature, many animals manage this at an astonishing rate – rabbits, for example, are notorious for their proclivity, but their efforts pale beside those of fish and insects. In the case of human beings, technology has made the traditional high birth-rate an undesirable thing. It's all very well for primitive peoples to have any number of children, since they all have short life-spans. But our current life expectancy is often three to four times longer than that of our ancestors only a few hundred years ago. As a result, excessive reproduction might even doom us as a species.

In the case of the Time Lords, this problem becomes magnified to a staggeringly high degree. If a Time Lord can live virtually forever (or even a mere ten thousand years) and could even have one child every other year, then we'd have a population explosion of mind-bending proportions on our hands in a few centuries. As a result of this line of thought, and due to the obvious fact that we aren't buried knee-deep in Time Lords' babies, it seems safe to conclude that Time Lords have a very low – and possibly non-existent – sex drive.

Certainly, every indication we have is to this end. The Doctor seems to have a liking for female companions, but his relations with them are strictly platonic. Even the Master, for all of his evil ways, seems not to have added either rape or seduction to his list of crimes. (Though he could certainly attempt them, as he manages very nicely with Galleia in The Time Monster, if only in a rather intellectual way.) So, despite a good deal of speculation on the part of some people, it seems safe to say that Time Lords as a species have no interest in sex after they regenerate. Given their languid lifestyles, probably few of them have any interest in it even before regeneration... For our sakes, we're very fortunate that this should be so; otherwise the Universe might well be filled with Time Lords by now...

CHAPTER 3:

TEMPORAL ENGINEERING

There have been, over the millennia, many forms of time travel devices used by the Time Lords. One of the more well-known is the TT Capsule: Time Travel Capsules, or, frequently, TARDISes. The acronym TARDIS was actually invented by the Doctor's granddaughter (known as Susan Foreman), and stands for Time And Relative Dimension In Space (though this is frequently misquoted as *Dimensions*). It is correctly applied only to the Type 40 model, though often inaccurately used to describe any TT Capsule of any model. Since the Time Lords themselves refer to the Type 40s as TARDISes, Susan presumably coined the expression before she and the Doctor fled Gallifrey.

The Type 40 is considered something of a classic model capsule and, due to its extreme age, it is also listed as a 'veteran and vintage vehicle'. Romana, for example, elected not to take a course in it at the Academy (*The Pirate Planet*). It is fitted with a chameleon circuit to change its appearance on landing. Not all Time Lord capsules can (or bother to) do this. In *The War Games*, we were shown SIDRATs, short-lived time capsules on the same general design as a TARDIS. They were featureless boxes, just over six feet on each side, with a single entry door. TARDISes possess many other sophistications often lacking in the streamlined later models. 305 were originally commissioned, but only one (the Doctor's TARDIS) remains functional – well, semi-functional at least. Both the Master and the Monk had later models, with added refinements. They were also fully functional, at least before the Doctor got his hands on them.

One of the most obvious points about the TARDIS is that it is larger inside than out. The Doctor often refers to this as being 'dimensionally transcendental'. He also claims that it is the Time Lords' greatest invention. In *The Time Monster*, he says that the

TARDIS 'has its being outside of time, but its appearance is here'. A TARDIS exists within a private time field of its own, which effectively causes it to exist in a separate dimension from our own.

The external shell of the Doctor's TARDIS.

The control room of the Master's TARDIS (*The Time Monster*).

Thus, it is easy to see why constructing a TARDIS was the Time Lords' greatest achievement. What they have managed is to create a sort of mobile private continuum of their own. Its interior and exterior dimensions do not overlap – the exterior is a sort of three-dimensional shadow cast by a multi-dimensional object. Technically, then, the TARDIS doesn't exist within our Universe. 'It's only the exterior of a TARDIS that exists as a real Space-Time event,' the Doctor explains to Adric (*Logopolis*). The doorway in and out is the only interface between the TARDIS and normal space-time. The Doctor can, in fact, switch his entry and exit point. He did this in *The Deadly Assassin* to escape the Chancellery Guard, and again when he moved from the old control room to the more baroque one (*The Masque of Mandragora*). It is merely a matter of aligning the fields.

Practically speaking, this 'private universe' inside a TARDIS leads to some interesting effects. First of all, it means that the interior of a TARDIS can be almost any size that the owner of the ship wants to make it. The Doctor's seems to be filled with many corridors and rooms, suiting his somewhat eccentric personality. The Master's, on the other hand, is much smaller and more spartan – he uses his TARDIS, rather than lives within it. Secondly, it can explain a

few of the properties of the TARDIS. In *The Hand of Fear*, the Doctor claims that the TARDIS exists in a state of 'temporal grace' that doesn't allow energy weapons to be fired within it. (This, however, didn't stop the Cybermen from using their weapons inside it in *Attack of The Cybermen*, nor the Sontarans from using theirs in *The Invasion of Time*. Presumably, in those cases the Doctor forgot to operate the right controls.) This implies that there is a form of energy damper inside the TARDIS that operates as a sort of general physical law within its own interior dimensions.

Thirdly, it would explain why the TARDIS is virtually indestructible. If the exterior of the TARDIS is little more than a shadow – no matter how solid – then very little could affect it. The TARDIS key is the only thing that can penetrate the boundaries between the exterior and interior Universes.

One thing we do know of that would probably destroy a TARDIS is Event One – the Big Bang that started all of Creation on its expanding journey. Given that the TARDIS is a stable alternative Universe, there is a clear reason why it should be affected by Event One (*The Edge of Destruction, Castrovalva*). Before the Big Bang, all matter was condensed into a tiny core, and nothing existed outside of it. This supremely dense matter would have a staggeringly high gravitational effect on the TARDIS, and undoubtedly cause it to either explode or implode into nothingness – either force a complete contraction of the TARDIS's own fields, or else the equivalent of a Big Bang, and scatter its atoms to create a new Universe itself, in neither case a pleasant thought for whoever might be within.

The TARDIS as a machine is so sophisticated and complex that in some way it possesses a personality – or, at least, a rudimentary form of consciousness. (When Mike Yates accuses the Doctor of speaking of the TARDIS 'as though she were alive', the Doctor's response is: 'Yes, I do, don't I?') They are equipped with telepathic circuits, which can enable two TARDISes to communicate with one another inside the maelstrom of the Space-Time Vortex. They are also in some degree of mental contact with their pilots. In *The Time Monster*, the TARDIS actually traces the Doctor while he is drifting in the Vortex, and with the help of Jo Grant, it can bring the Doctor aboard. In *The Edge of Destruction*, the TARDIS attempts to warn the Doctor of impending doom by flashing a series of pictures on the screen. It cannot communicate in words, and must resort to roundabout methods to contact people. The Doctor, Susan, Ian and Barbara are all suffering from headaches in this story, possibly caused by the TARDIS attempting to contact them directly through the telepathic circuits – which were undoubtedly one of the systems that suffered the massive failures that stranded the Doctor on the Earth in 1963.

Another way for it to communicate with the Doctor is the use of the Cloister Bell (*Logopolis*), which rings to suggest impending destruction. The Cloister Bell is located somewhere around the Cloister Room, where the Doctor often retreats to meditate or simply to relax.

Though TARDISes do not occupy space as such in our continuum, they cannot share the same absolute space. The Doctor, for example, has materialized his TARDIS within the Master's TARDIS (*The Time Monster, Logopolis*). This has resulted in the strange (by normal standards) occurrence that both TARDISes end up inside one another – and that it is possible to cross over from one to another in an almost endless series of progressions. This is because of the odd effects of overlapping the two dimensional fields almost exactly. However, if the two fields overlap

exactly, then a very different and disastrous state occurs – that of Time Ram. When two TARDISes operating on the same frequency occupy exactly the same coordinates in space and time, then the result is a catastrophic explosion, and mutual annihilation of both devices and their occupants.

The TARDIS has a built-in data core, which contains the computerized information necessary for it to steer and maintain itself. Theoretically, it is possible to steer a TARDIS to any given position in time and space. Practically, however, it is a matter of knowing the exact coordinates. Needless to say, this is not a simple matter. When the Doctor 'borrowed' his TARDIS, it was already malfunctioning. The instructions manual was missing although the Doctor had either found it or taken another by the time of *The Pirate Planet*. The Doctor did not know exactly how to operate the TARDIS – it was a practical

The second Doctor at the control console of his TARDIS (*The War Games*).

subject he'd never really needed to know in the past. Accordingly, he had to allow the TARDIS to take its own paths through the Vortex.

The TARDIS's data core contains a total of 18,348 emergency instructions (*State of Decay*). Given the extreme caution of the Time Lords, many of these will be for events that are never likely to happen. Not all of the information needed to operate the TARDIS is contained within the data core, though, which is a relatively recent invention. It was probably used in the Type 40 for the first time. Older capsules used much less sophisticated methods of data storage, such as punched cards.

In periods of emergency, there is the possibility of generating extra power by jettisoning some of the interior space of the TARDIS. The Doctor was forced to eject Romana's old room (*Logopolis*) for this reason, and then fully a quarter of the TARDIS's rooms (*Castrovalva*) to escape from Event One. One of the rooms that was lost was the Zero Room. This is a Time Lord invention of great simplicity, a room that excludes all outside forces (including gravity, if so desired), in order to allow a Time Lord to relax completely. Because their minds are capable of picking up thoughts, such an invention is necessary for total relaxation.

In addition to the TT Capsules, the Time Lords have other time travel technology. In *Genesis of the Daleks*, the Time Lords give the Doctor a Time Ring. It is a pretty simple device, merely acting like a

Tegan, Nyssa and the fifth Doctor in the Zero Room of the TARDIS (*Castrovalva*).

homing beacon to return him to the TARDIS, but it operated across time and space to do so.

The Time Lords based on Gallifrey do not need to use any travel machine, it would seem, to make a simple hop. In *Terror of the Autons* and *Genesis of the Daleks,* for example, a Time Lord meets with the Doctor simply by being physically projected from Gallifrey. We are never told quite how this is done, but is clearly quite a simple matter for beings as sophisticated as the Time Lords. Provided they know its exact coordinates, they can also snatch a TARDIS out of time and space. They can also manipulate the flow of time, throwing up time-damping force-fields (*The War Games*).

Speculations

Perhaps the telepathic circuits explain how the Doctor and his companions can speak the local language when they arrive in the TARDIS. It is possible that the TARDIS scans the minds of the closest natives in the moment before it materializes and then implants this information in the minds of the travellers. (It would, of convenience, wipe the knowledge out when they leave, otherwise they'd have serious problems after a hundred landings...)

The Doctor's only reference to the ability to speak other languages is in The Masque Of Mandragora, *where he simply says that Sarah can speak Italian as 'a Time Lord gift'.*

It may also explain why the Doctor always seems to land in trouble – the TARDIS is taking him where it knows the Doctor is needed. He does also seem often to run into the Master at just the right time to stop his latest plans – and given the vastness of space and time open to both of them, this can hardly be coincidental. And perhaps it explains why the TARDIS generally lands in a secluded or unobserved spot – it picks a place where there are no people currently standing. Of course, since the TARDIS often malfunctions, this isn't invariably adhered to. In Planet Of The Spiders *the Doctor tells Mike Yates that 'I always leave the actual landings to the TARDIS. She's no fool, you know.'*

CHAPTER 4:

THE MATRIX

One of the great achievements of the Time Lords is the APC Net – the Amplified Panatropic Computations Network. It is located in the Capital, and is a masterpiece of exitonic engineering, consisting of billions of artificial brain cells. When a Time Lord is dying, his mind can be linked to the Net, and his knowledge duplicated into the system. The combined knowledge of innumerable Time Lords exists within this unit. It serves to monitor life in the Capital, and to perform many computational functions. It may also analyze events and predict forthcoming events.

It did, for example, predict the impending assassination of the President by the Master (though the Master diverted this prediction to the Doctor alone, in *The Deadly Assassin*). It also predicted a potential future in which the Daleks become sole masters of the Universe (*Genesis of the Daleks*).

It is possible for a still-living mind to be connected to the Matrix – the 'landscape' within the APC Net. There are two legal ways for this to be accomplished. One is through the input that scans the dying brains. This is quite painful, however, and not everyone can survive it. The second method is through the headband worn by the President of the Time Lords, using which he can safely commune with the Net, and draw on its vast supply of knowledge to aid him in his decisions. His mind becomes permanently a part of the Matrix in this fashion, and thus when he dies, his knowledge lives on. The mind-patterns of all previous Presidents of the Time Lords are thus a part of the APC Net. It is simply a matter of being able to access them. This record stretches back to the earliest known period of the Time Lords' history, including that of Rassilon.

There are illegal ways into the Matrix, of course. The Master used one such connection for his puppet,

Goth, in *The Deadly Assassin*. The Valeyard knew of another, the half-legendary seventh entrance in *The Trial of a Time Lord*.

The sixth Doctor, on trial for his life because of false evidence planted in the Matrix (*The Trial of a Time Lord*).

The Matrix contains all the knowledge accumulated by the Time Lords. It can be entered mentally only by a person acclimatized to it, and access is generally limited to the President of the High Council. Even then, he must be mentally and physically alert in order to safely enter the APC Net, which places a great drain on his faculties. The Matrix can also reject people who are mentally incompatible with it. On the other hand, the Matrix has been invaded numerous times by other Time Lords; the Master (*The Deadly Assassin*, *The Trial of a Time Lord*), Omega (*Arc of Infinity*) and the Valeyard (*The Trial of a Time Lord*). Even aliens have managed to penetrate it, as in the case of the Vardans (*The Invasion of Time*). Once again, it would seem that the Time Lords' 'facts' are quite mutable: despite their claim that only the President can enter the Matrix, this is quite clearly untrue.

The Bio Scan data of all living Time Lords is held inside the Matrix. Theoretically it is accessible only to the President of the Council. On the other hand, both Councillor Hedin (*Arc of Infinity*) and the Master

(*The Deadly Assassin*) have stolen the Doctor's data from it. It is simply a matter of knowing (or deducing) the correct codes to gain access.

Originally, the Bio Scans (then called Data Extracts or DEs) were separate from the Matrix (*The Deadly Assassin*), but they proved to be too susceptible to interference and change. As a result, they were then adapted into the APC Net. This did not make them all that much safer in fact, but undoubtedly it made the Time Lords breathe a little easier.

The Time Lords scan the reaches of space and time, accumulating information at a rate far greater than any minds could comprehend. Scanning beams are thus linked into the Matrix, and all of the information gathered by the scans is stored within the Matrix. Generally speaking, this is a safe process, but on one occasion it almost spelled the doom of the Time Lords. One such scanning beam touched upon the home world of the Vardans.

Though a humanoid race, the Vardans possess the

The Master connecting Chancellor Goth into the Matrix (*The Deadly Assassin*).

The Vardans, who invaded Gallifrey through the Matrix (*The Invasion of Time*).

Coordinator Engin and Castellan Spandrell preparing the fourth Doctor for entry into the Matrix.

ability to transform themselves and travel down any broadcast wavelengths, including those of thought. When the scans touched their world, several Vardans managed to trace back along the path and invade the Matrix. They then sought to enlist the aid of a renegade Time Lord in order to invade Gallifrey physically. They made a grave error in their choice, selecting the Doctor. Though he played along with their plans, he managed to shield his true thoughts from them. He used his robotic companion, K9, to link with the Matrix and search it for information and the point of entry used by the Vardans.

Once he had found this, K9 could then activate the rejection of the Vardans from the Matrix, and trigger a time bubble about their home world. The Vardans thus remain sealed within their home planet forever.

The Valeyard seized control of the Matrix in his own attempt to kill the Doctor and the members of the Ultimate Court of Appeal (*The Ultimate Foe*). During this time, we were shown a new figure, the Keeper of the Matrix. Though his precise function was never made clear, he seems to have been a recent appoint-

ment, whose job was to ensure that only authorized persons had access to the Matrix. He didn't perform his tasks at all well, since both the Master and the Valeyard had their own channels of entry, and both manipulated the Matrix as they wished. The Doctor managed temporarily to freeze the Matrix, trapping the Master. The Valeyard, however, used his own connection with the Matrix to take over the body of the Keeper.

We are also told in this tale that the Matrix has not merely the ability to predict the future, but actual knowledge of it. Presumably it has been upgraded in the intervening years, and can now collect data from the future time streams. The Time Lords have also recently placed collecting devices within each TT Capsule (including the Doctor's, which they didn't bother to tell him about). These 'bugs' have a fair range, and can collect information and transmit it back to the Matrix on Gallifrey for recording and evaluation. In the Doctor's case, it provided the 'evidence' used in his trial. This information had, of course, been severely edited before it was presented as evidence.

CHAPTER 5:

POLITICS

Since the political systems of the Time Lords have changed over the millennia, what follows is only a brief description of how the Time Lords organize and govern their society. However, as has been noted, Time Lords are very averse to change, and thus the following data is accurate for a long stretch of their history.

The families of High Gallifrey are split into a number of Chapters. The origin of these Chapters is shrouded in mystery, and may have grown from workers' guilds or unions, or perhaps from family groupings. Currently there are a large number of these Chapters, though only three, the Prydonians, the Archalians and the Patrexes, are of any real political significance. Of the three, the Prydonian Chapter is both the largest and the most influential. It has given rise to more Presidents than all of the other Chapters combined, and a very high number of the politicians and movers of Time Lord society are from this Chapter.

There are other, more plebeian, classes of society, but these are not Time Lords. They are the common folk of Gallifrey, the lowest of whom are known as the Sheboogans – considered lazy, feckless and often criminal. Naturally, the Time Lords have as little contact as possible with these members of society, and are not terribly interested in the way that those beings run or organize their lives.

The highest echelons of the hierarchy of each Chapter are allowed seats in the Panopticon, where they sit in formal, flowing robes, and high-backed collars. Their clothing is colour-coded to show their Chapters: Prydonians wear scarlet and orange, Archalians wear green, and Patrexes wear heliotrope (a light purple). The right to a seat in the Panopticon

is mostly ceremonial, as the Time Lords are inordinately fond of pomp and show. There is little actual power held even by the ranking Time Lords. In charge of the formal events held within the Panopticon is the Gold Usher. He is generally a venerable Time Lord, chosen for the respect in which he is held. Since his is largely a ceremonial office, the Gold Usher holds no real political power. His responsibility is to ensure that ceremony is adhered to on all formal occasions such as the investiture or resignation of the President.

> ### 'They like making speeches.'
> THE DOCTOR, *THE WAR GAMES*

Each Chapter is represented by a Cardinal, who sits on the Time Lord Council, where the power begins finally to be real. From this Council are selected members of the High Council – usually at least five people. These can be either Cardinals or Chancellors. Chancellors are the day-to-day power in the Chapters, in charge of actually running the affairs of the Chapter that they serve. Thus Chancellors are almost always competent and sometimes brutally efficient. Cardinals, on the other hand, are often chosen more for their age, learning and wisdom than for efficiency.

The High Council, at least in theory, acts as advisers to the President. It is also empowered to depose the President for just cause, and to appoint temporary successors to this post. They are also able to out-vote the President in some matters. Frequently – especially in the case of a weak President – the Council actually rules Gallifrey. Before Borusa became the President, for example, he had been on the Council, and gained his power there. He preferred – at least initially – to manipulate the reins of power from behind the scenes.

From within the High Council, two members can sit with the President to form the Inner Council.

The fourth Doctor in the robes of the Prydonian Chapter (*The Deadly Assassin*).

was a politician, more concerned with regulations and appearances than with operations and work. When the renegade Omega attacked Gallifrey, the President decided to use past incarnations of the Doctor to help the present one. The Chancellor's reaction was one of horror: the First Law of Time expressly forbids a Time Lord to meet himself. Despite this, the President pressed ahead with his plan. This was the only time that the President was shown to be in anything less than full control of Gallifrey.

By the time of *The Deadly Assassin,* much of this hierarchy in the Time Lords has altered. The President is now in charge of everything, but his post is no longer technical. It is almost purely political. Just how much objective time has passed between the two tales is hard to estimate, but it is clearly more than a few years. The President is an elected official, from some senior position in the High Council. However, this election is not of the general populace, but from within the Council itself. The outgoing President normally appoints his own successor. There is no indication that he has even to bother conferring with the High Council to determine who the next President will be. The only time that a general election is held is when the President dies in office without naming a successor.

Article 17 of the Constitution then guarantees that anyone who then wishes to run for the office of the President may do so. They cannot be impeded in any way in their bid for office. As a result, surprising shifts in Time Lord power can be achieved through an election of this nature – and rarely, if ever, at any other time.

Obviously, though, the politicians in current power do not approve of this method of succession – it is far too unsettling. Normally, a President resigns from office after a long term – often lasting hundreds of years, as in the case of Pandak III, and he then nominates his own successor. This achieves a continuity of power and policy – and explains why the Time Lords so often seem stagnant, as succeeding Presidents often simply continue the policies of the previous incumbent. Real shifts in Time Lord policies only occur at the rare election times.

The President holds the symbols of office: the Sash of Rassilon and the Great Key, which is normally stored in a display case in the Panopticon. Their original purpose was forgotten over the centuries, until the Doctor and the Master revealed it in the

Together they can take control at times of great emergency. Such occurrences are very rare indeed.

There are any number of minor and major offices to which individuals may be posted. One of these is that of the Surgeon General. One of his main tasks is to ensure the health of the President and other ranking members of the High Council.

It is in *The Three Doctors* that we are first shown the internal affairs of Gallifrey, as it became menaced by the threat of Omega. The central hub of Time Lord power is the Time Control Room. In ultimate charge of operations there is the President of the Council. His post is clearly shown to be of a technical nature – he understands and controls the technicians that staff the room. This role of his was not to last too long, and may simply have been due to the current President being an unusually active person.

Above him – at least theoretically – in the hierarchy of Time Lords was the Chancellor. This person

Leela, companion of the fourth Doctor, and Captain Andred of the Chancellery Guard (*The Invasion of Time*).

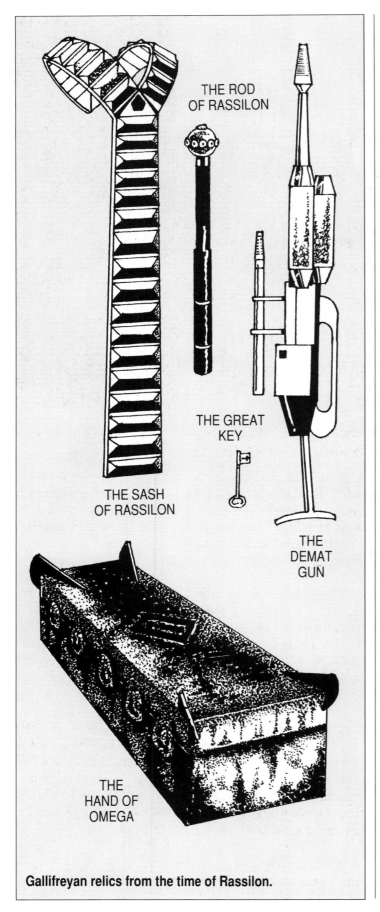

THE ROD
OF RASSILON

THE GREAT
KEY

THE SASH
OF RASSILON

THE
DEMAT
GUN

THE
HAND OF
OMEGA

Gallifreyan relics from the time of Rassilon.

affair of *The Deadly Assassin*. There is a second Great Key, which is held in secret by the Chancellor, and which must be used in conjunction with the Sash of Rassilon and the Rod of Rassilon in order to control the full power of the Time Lords.

In charge of security is the Castellan, a Time Lord of rank, and inevitably a member of the High Council. This is more a position of political appointment than of true ability, and over the centuries there have been several Castellans who have been less than worthy of the high post. Notable among these was Kelner. This politically ambitious person cooperated fully with both the Vardans and the Sontarans when each of them invaded Gallifrey (*The Invasion of Time*). He was finally tried and executed for his treachery.

The Chancellery Guards, under the command of the Castellan, are the only beings allowed to carry arms inside the Citadel. They are not, however, Time Lords themselves. This is probably due to the hazardous nature of their job – few Time Lords would wish to risk their near-immortality by undertaking anything like a dangerous job. In *Arc of Infinity,* Commander Maxil is shown as being eager to execute a Time Lord, and views this impending execution as an outsider privileged to kill one of the elite. Also, Andred (*The Invasion of Time*) is allowed to marry a non-Gallifreyan, Leela – by implication stating that he is, like her, a mere mortal.

The execution of a Time Lord is a very rare event, and can be carried out only after the necessary warrant is issued. As with everything else, protocol must be observed, and the Time Lords have a set format for everything, even the execution of one of their own. The method of execution is almost invariably vaporization.

Time Lords can be placed on trial for a number of offences, and since they have a great many laws, they invariably have a great deal of potential crimes of varying degrees of venality. Sentences then imposed vary considerably. When the Doctor was originally captured and tried by the Time Lords, he expected his own punishment to be little more than a good, stiff lecture (*The War Games*), and probably being compelled to stay on Gallifrey until he could slip off again. However, there are various grades of punishments. Exile from Gallifrey for a set period of time is a favourite punishment, and has been passed on a number of Time Lords. For the tradition-loving, self-indulgent general run-of-the-mill Time Lords, such

The War Lord, the second Doctor, Jamie and Zoe at the trial of the War Lord (*The War Games*).

exile is a terrible punishment, and its threat serves as an effective deterrent to many. However, there are always those of Time Lord rank who find the pomp, ceremony and lethargic attitudes of Gallifrey stultifying – and who welcome their exiles, and even anticipate it by leaving early.

Trials of Time Lords are taken very seriously. The Doctor's first was a Malfeasance Tribunal (dated 309906); as a result of it he was exiled to Earth, known to the Time Lords as Sol 3 of the Mutters Spiral. His initial period of exile resulted in a pardon, issued after the intervention of the CIA: the Celestial Intervention Agency.

The Doctor's second trial was a far more serious one. In this, the High Council appointed an Inquisitor to try him. The Inquisitor was empowered to sift the evidence and cases presented by the prosecutor, the Valeyard, and to pronounce sentence on the Doctor. Had he been found guilty, he would have been exterminated. Few Time Lords have ever been judicially executed by their own race – even the Master was merely imprisoned for his crimes. The only other known case of execution of a Time Lord was that of the rebel Morbius.

The Doctor managed to avoid his own execution. With the help of the Master, the Doctor was able to prove that the trial was a sham, the charges spurious and that the prosecutor was in fact the Doctor's shadowy evil self. He was this time exonerated of all charges.

There is an Ultimate Court of Appeal, which is served by the most senior jurists in the Time Lord race, whose task it is to uphold the fundamentals of Gallifreyan law. These have been laid down in the Gallifreyan Constitution – like most Time Lord edicts, a long, rambling and complex document almost impossible for one being to understand fully.

The CIA is a very secret, shadowy group. They stand pretty much outside the Laws of Time, and do not answer even to the President or High Council. It is virtually impossible to be certain who may or may not be working for them, and nothing is known of their power or scope of operations, although some of their policy decisions are quite apparent.

They care nothing for the trappings of power, and are content to leave the everyday affairs of Gallifrey in the hands of the President. They are concerned

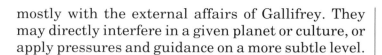

mostly with the external affairs of Gallifrey. They may directly interfere in a given planet or culture, or apply pressures and guidance on a more subtle level.

Although the CIA was mentioned in only one story – *The Deadly Assassin* – it is to be supposed that after the trial of the Doctor and his exile, they used him on a number of occasions to do their dirty work for them. In none of these cases was he consulted, or even met by a member of the CIA, although he was never left in any doubt as to what they wished him to do. Examples of the cases that the Doctor has been forced to undertake on their behalf are the recovery or destruction of the Doomsday Device (*Colony in Space*); aiding the planet Solos in its attempts to become independent of the Earth (*The Mutants*) and helping the Sisterhood of Karn rekindle their Sacred Flame (*The Brain of Morbius*).

As with every race, not all Time Lords have benevolent aims, and many political figures seek office for the worst of reasons. Over the millennia there have been many political scandals on Gallifrey, of which the worst was the revelation that the entire High Council had been corrupted (*The Trial of a Time Lord*). In an attempt to cover up their own mistakes and criminal activities, they were willing to sacrifice the lives of millions of human beings, to manipulate time, and to break the First Law of Time with regard to the Doctor. To cover their tracks, they instigated the creation of the Valeyard and attempted to kill the Doctor, knowing he was getting close to discovering the truth of their tawdry careers.

Instead, their plans did not work as the population of Gallifrey became aware of their treachery. For the first time ever, there was a popular revolution that tore the corrupt politicians from power and imprisoned them to face the very tribunal that they had assembled to try the Doctor. In their place, a new regime – one proven to be incorrupt and untouchable – was elected. It now seems that Gallifrey has entered upon a period of inner searching and outward tranquillity. How long this will last is impossible to tell.

The sixth Doctor faces the court at his second trial (*The Trial of a Time Lord*).

CHAPTER 6:

CHAPTER 6:
THE DOCTOR AND THE TIME LORDS

> ## 'Curiosity is his weakness.'
> ### THE MASTER, *TERROR OF THE AUTONS*

Of all the renegades of the Time Lord race, perhaps none is better known than the Doctor. (The term 'renegade', it must be stressed, refers only to Time Lords who have left the planet Gallifrey for their own reasons; it does not imply any villainy on their part.) His own conscience drove him to flee his home world, and he seems to have been influenced by – and in his turn, to have influenced – many about him.

The Doctor was born about a thousand years ago to a Prydonian family that lived on South Gallifrey, in a house perched half-way up a mountainside. At the peak of the mountain lived a hermit in a cave. On one occasion when the Doctor was feeling crushed by some unknown misfortune (*The Time Monster*), he climbed the mountain to seek guidance from the hermit. The holy man merely pointed to a small weed, and the Doctor saw it through his eyes – as absolutely glowing with life. The young Doctor understood the meaning of the older man's message – that life isn't something to be endured, but something we are given that must be treasured as long as we possess it. Over the years, the Doctor learned much from this hermit, including how to seek within himself for the truth. The hermit – who possessed a streak of humour unusual for a Time Lord – also enjoyed telling the Doctor ghost stories. In later years, the hermit also left Gallifrey, and once again encountered the Doctor, this time on the Earth. (See Chapter 17.)

At school, the Doctor committed many of the boyhood mischiefs normal for a Time Lord, such as building time jammers out of bric-a-brac in order to ruin the temporal experiments of others.

The fourth Doctor is arrested on suspicion of assassinating the President (*The Deadly Assassin*).

The Doctor, being a member of the Prydonian Chapter, attended the Academy, where he studied under many famous tutors, including Borusa. Among his contemporaries there were the Master, the Rani and Drax. Since all three of these also left Gallifrey, we may wonder if there was not some form of student protest against the hierarchy in those days. The Doctor finally graduated on the second attempt with 51% in the class of '92. This low mark was not due to any lack of intelligence or skill, but to the fact that he was so easily distracted at the time, presumably by political causes. (His own excuse was that he was a late developer.) He was already about 300 years old at this time. Given that Romana graduated at about the age of 125, it would seem that the Doctor had deliberately drawn out his time at the Academy.

The Doctor soon decided that he could tolerate Gallifrey no longer. 'I was bored,' he admitted honestly to Jamie and Zoe in *The War Games*. His people had immense power, but virtually never used it. They were mostly content simply to observe other species. They developed a strict rule against interference, and only violated this edict on special occasions, usually in order to answer some pressing circumstance. They outlawed the Scope (*Carnival of Monsters*) because it imprisoned sentient beings for the amusement of jaded appetites and manipulated their lives. They destroyed the planet between Mars and Jupiter in the Solar System to try to isolate the Fendahleen (*Image of The Fendahl*). Generally, however, they stayed aloof from other races, and had a strict edict against any Time Lord violating this decision.

Initially, the Doctor was acting simply out of boredom – or so he claimed. He stole a TARDIS that was in the bays for repairs, and he and his granddaughter, Susan, fled Gallifrey in it. In *The Pirate Planet*, Romana tells us that the Doctor had at that point been using the TARDIS for 523 years, so this meant he was about 300 when he left his home world. The Doctor had never piloted one of the TT Capsules before, and was forced to rely heavily on his notebooks for the codes of operation. Systems malfunctions didn't help, and one gigantic failure of the entire TARDIS left the Doctor and Susan stranded for several months on Earth in 1963. Though he managed to perform makeshift repairs, the TARDIS didn't work properly, and the loss of his notes on the prehistoric Earth (*The Tribe of Gum*) sealed his fate to wander.

This suited the Doctor perfectly, as he had no set aims or destinations anyway. It also made tracking his progress considerably more difficult for the Time Lords.

He had begun his travels because of boredom, but he soon developed a new motivation. He came into contact with the presence of evil, and his carefully maintained Time Lord veneer of aloofness and indifference began to thaw as the Doctor came to know, understand and finally both like and admire his human travelling companions. It became impossible for him to stand on the sidelines and merely observe, as he had been trained to do. He witnessed evil forces at work – forces like the Yeti, the Quarks, the Cybermen and the Daleks. He became a passionate champion of justice, and sloughed off all of his old indifference. He had become a different person from the one who had left Gallifrey to escape boredom. He had also broken all of the Time Lords' most sacred laws.

Finally, in his quest, he stumbled across the plans of the War Lord and his minions. Alien conquerors, they had joined forces with a renegade of the Doctor's own race, a being known as the War Chief, who had given them SIDRAT machines he had stolen from Gallifrey. The War Lord had used them to steal soldiers from some of the Earth's bloodiest wars, and took them to the various zones of an alien world. There the War Lord, the War Chief and the Security Chief had staged the War Games, designed to refine the kidnapped humans into an unbeatable force, with which they would then take over the Galaxy.

The Doctor managed to defeat their plans, but he was left in a very difficult dilemma. The SIDRATs had very limited travel life, and all but two had worn out. There was simply no way that he could return the kidnapped humans to their own time periods. His only choice was to call in the Time Lords for help.

Though he had cut off most of the contacts he had had with his own race, he still carried with him the pieces of a psychic beacon. Assembling this using telepathy, he encoded it with all of the information that the Time Lords needed to stop the Games and return the humans home. Unfortunately, it also enabled the Time Lords to trace him, and to hold him for trial.

When forced to intervene, the Time Lords could be most effective. They placed the War Lord on trial for his crimes of gross inhumanity. When he proved that they were correct in their reading of his ruthlessness and lack of remorse, they dematerialized him, erasing his past, so that it was if he and his forces had never existed. They then threw a barrier around his home world, sealing the alien race forever from leaving their home and infecting the rest of the Galaxy.

Then it was the turn of the Doctor to stand trial for his actions. He didn't merely defend himself; he attacked the Time Lords' policy of strict non-interference. 'While you have been content to observe the evil in the Galaxy, I have been fighting against it,' he told them. He accused them of failing to use their great powers wisely.

'You have raised difficult issues,' he was told. 'We require time to think about them.' In the end, the period of discussion was short. With certain reservations, the court agreed with the Doctor. There was evil in the Universe, and it should be fought against, not merely observed. The Doctor clearly had a role to play in this fight, and was definitely interested in continuing the war on evil he had begun. Accordingly, the Time Lords sentenced him to exile for his actions. They removed his knowledge of time travel, and confined his TARDIS to Earth in a small portion of the late twentieth century. They also imposed a regeneration upon him.

From time to time, they then called upon his help in certain missions. They began with small items, getting the Doctor to play little more than the role of messenger boy for them. Finally, after the Doctor saved the entire world of Gallifrey and the civilization of the Time Lords from destruction at the hands of Omega, they relented and restored his knowledge and freedom to travel in time and space. This was partly as a reward and partly because it had become obvious to them that the Doctor was much more useful to their policies when he working as a free agent.

The Doctor has twice been appointed to the Presidency of the Time Lords. The first instance was during the affair of *The Deadly Assassin* when the Doctor presented himself as a candidate for the Presidency as a ploy to prevent his own execution. There was only one other candidate for the post, Goth, whose election was widely expected to be a mere formality. Instead, it was revealed that Goth was no more than a pawn being used by the Master, and Goth was casually slain when the Master's plans went awry. Though the Master was defeated, the Doctor was thus left as the President elect by default.

Since the Doctor left Gallifrey almost immediately, he was never actually sworn in at the time as the President. In his place, Borusa became the Acting Chancellor, and ruled Gallifrey with the aid of the High Council. When the Doctor discovered the plans of the Vardans to invade Gallifrey after breaching the Matrix (*The Invasion of Time*), he formulated a plan to defeat them that entailed his taking office as President. He was inducted into the post, and used it to defeat the Vardans and their masters, the Sontarans. Then he once again fled Gallifrey, leaving the task of ruling the planet in the hands of Borusa.

Borusa ultimately proved to be corrupt, and was removed from power by the direct intervention of the legendary Rassilon himself. The High Council then promptly appointed the Doctor once again to the Presidency in Borusa's place. Rather than face the task of ruling Gallifrey, the Doctor appointed Lady Flavia to temporary power in his place, and went on the run once again.

This time, though, the Doctor was legally stricken from the office of the Presidency, since it was quite clear that he never aimed to take on the post. He was replaced by an unknown figure who proved to be probably the most corrupt President that the Time Lords have ever known. Both the President and the High Council were overthrown in a popular revolution (*The Trial of a Time Lord*). The Inquisitor asked the Doctor to stand for the Presidency once again, but the Doctor refused.

Speculation

The Doctor had managed to remain hidden from the Time Lords during his first and second incarnations. How he had managed this is unclear, since both the Elders (The Savages) and the Daleks (The Chase and The Daleks' Masterplan) had managed to track

him down. Not only that, but another Time Lord, the Monk, also tracked the Doctor's TARDIS through the Vortex. However, the Doctor eluded his fellow Time Lords until he was forced to summon their help in The War Games. Once he had been found, the Time Lords

The third, second, fifth and first Doctors in the tomb of Rasillon (*The Five Doctors*).

The first appearance of the Doctor's old mentor Borusa was in _The Deadly Assassin_.

could then use their current knowledge of the Doctor to trace his past adventures. They could then use this information to gain a time fix on both of the earlier incarnations of the Doctor.

By their own laws, they should not have interfered with the Doctor's past life. The emergency with Omega, however, prevented them from abiding too closely by their own rules. They were forced to act retroactively upon the Doctor, and thus began their long process of altering the Doctor's own history. It was now no longer possible for the Doctor simply to be another Time Lord. His own past had been changed, and he was in the process of being metamorphosed into something very different...

His previous incarnations now had a firm knowledge of their own future selves, and this was one that they retained in their contemporary lives. In The Five Doctors, for example, the second Doctor recalled the events that had happened in The Three Doctors – which were (theoretically) still in his own future. And in The Two Doctors, the second Doctor is sent on a mission for the Time Lords – who had never managed to actually trace him during his real lifetime. The

final result of the Time Lords' meddling in the Doctor's lives was to manifest itself in the creation of the Valeyard.

The Doctor is no longer quite the Time Lord that he once was. He is, as it were, somewhat dislocated in time because of the actions of his own race. His past has been altered, and so has his future. In The Trial of a Time Lord, the Doctor examines his own future and relates an adventure that will someday take place involving a companion, Mel. But by the end of his trial, Mel – with a full knowledge of what is supposed to be still future events for the Doctor – joins the Doctor as a companion. So not only the Doctor's past has been changed, but also his own future.

The seventh Doctor has also dropped hints that he is not simply a Time Lord any longer. He mentions having worked with Rassilon (Remembrance of The Daleks, and Nemesis (Silver Nemesis) clearly knows things about the Doctor's past that the Doctor does not want to be revealed. Is this because the Doctor was always someone other than he had claimed to be? Or is it because he has become someone else? Clearly, there is still plenty of mystery surrounding the Doctor.

Susan, the Doctor's first companion.

CHAPTER 7:

SUSAN

Susan is the Doctor's granddaughter. When he made his decision to leave Gallifrey, he was reluctant to leave her behind, and so took her with him. The Doctor's original aim was simply to run, without a destination in mind, and he 'borrowed' a battered old Type 40 machine. Unfamiliar with the controls, he was forced to utilize a notebook in which he had copied down the operational codes in order to have any control over the old ship. Susan had in fact been the person who had invented the acronym TARDIS used to describe the TT Capsules – Time And Relative Dimension In Space.

Some of the travels the Doctor and Susan undertook together are unrecorded. There is mention of a stay on the planet Quinnis (in *The Edge of Destruction*), and she had obviously visited France at the time of the French Revolution (the Doctor apparently enjoyed the attempts to overthrow a corrupt ruling body and install a rational system), but little is known of their other adventures together. However, Susan clearly did not like their restless meanderings throughout time and space as much as the Doctor. When the TARDIS suffered a massive systems failure and crash-landed on Earth in 1963, she was more than glad to settle down to lead a 'normal' life there.

The TARDIS had arrived in a deserted junkyard in Totter's Lane, London, originally owned by a mysterious I.M. Foreman. Adopting the surname, Susan was able to enter the local Coal Hill School. She soon found the pace of life there to her liking, though she did not make friends. Unable to invite anyone home with her – how could she explain that the police box was her home? – she tended to be lonely and aloof. But she found the primitive simplicity of the time to be

> **STORIES:**
> *The Tribe of Gum*
> *The Daleks*
> *The Edge of Destruction*
> *Marco Polo*
> *The Keys of Marinus*
> *The Aztecs*
> *The Sensorites*
> *The Reign of Terror*
> *Planet of Giants*
> *The Dalek Invasion of Earth*
> *The Five Doctors*

fascinating. She loved the London fogs, and the perverse safety that night cast over the city.

Unhappily, her alien nature led to trouble. She was terribly ignorant of the conditions of the day, since most of her information about the Earth had been picked up on her various travels, and was not always either accurate or organized. She muddled her time-periods, and exactly what was known of science and history. In the end, her strange manners and knowledge raised suspicions in the minds of two of her teachers, Barbara Wright and Ian Chesterton. They followed her home one evening, and stumbled into the freshly-repaired TARDIS.

Susan's dreams of settling – at least for a while – in the twentieth century were dashed. The Doctor, afraid of exposure and perhaps even discovery by the Time Lords, set the TARDIS in flight again, carrying off the two teachers as well as himself and Susan. When the TARDIS landed them in the Stone Age, a run-in with the primitive inhabitants resulted in the loss of the Doctor's notebook. Thereafter, he was completely unable to programme the ship, and its meanderings were even more random than before.

Susan, however, finally had friends. Barbara and Ian – initially furious with the Doctor – finally settled into a truce. Susan interceded on their behalf with her grandfather. After an incident in which the TARDIS was almost destroyed (*The Edge of Destruction*), the Doctor finally made peace with the two teachers. The Doctor's initial suspicion and dislike of the two teachers mellowed, and he began to see that even so-called 'primitives' from Earth were people in their own right. His own prejudices were con-

Susan and her friend Ping-Cho (*Marco Polo*).

fronted, and he began to acquire the more mature outlook that soon began to characterize him. Susan, too, found the companionship of the two teachers to be rewarding. For the first time in her short life, she had friends that she could confide in and who supported her.

She still lacked real contact with anyone of her own age, until the TARDIS took them to the year AD 1289, and she met the Chinese girl, Ping-Cho. The young woman was on her way to be married, and she and Susan struck up a friendship. More and more as their enforced journey with the Venetian traveller Marco Polo progressed, Susan began to feel what it was like to settle down and to enjoy the company of people her own age. She and Ping-Cho were forced to say their goodbyes as the TARDIS took the Doctor and friends onwards, but Susan never forgot the young girl.

By the time of their arrival on the Sense-Sphere (*The Sensorites*), Susan's outlook had broadened considerably. To the Doctor's frustration and annoyance, Susan began for the first time to question his judgment and opinions. In the past, she had always deferred to him, but now things were changing, and this disturbed the Doctor greatly. As the two teachers realized, Susan was growing up. She was looking for her own identity.

Forced to deal with this, the Doctor took a deep, hard look at his granddaughter and her aims and desires. She clearly did not enjoy the wandering life that he did, and she also longed for companionship and stability in her life. Reluctantly, the Doctor was forced to make the very hard decision – to leave Susan behind at the first real chance.

It was very wrenching for him, but he had to be selfless about the decision. Susan was clearly unhappy in their travels. If she stayed behind, then there was very little chance that the Time Lords would ever find her. Their tracking efforts would be centred on locating the TARDIS, and no matter how observant they might be, there was virtually no chance that they would ever find Susan if she were separated from the TARDIS.

Ian, the first Doctor, Barbara and Susan with the crew of the Earth space ship from *The Sensorites*.

The Doctor's moment of crisis came in the year AD 2167. The Daleks had conquered and devastated the Earth, and the Doctor and his friends became involved with the rebels fighting to destroy the Daleks and to reclaim their world. Susan became enmeshed with the fighters, and especially with young David Campbell, one of their leaders. Soon she had clearly fallen in love with him, and he with her.

Susan re-united with the first Doctor in the Death Zone on Gallifrey (*The Five Doctors*).

With the defeat of the Daleks, Susan was prepared to travel on, thinking that her grandfather needed her help to get along. The Doctor, however, made the decision he had been dreading – he locked her out of the TARDIS, and forced her to remain behind with David. Hard as it was for him, he knew that the challenge of rebuilding a civilization would be more in Susan's best interests than in further accompanying him on his meandering journey.

Susan settled down to marry David, and to be a farmer's wife in the new order. Along with the other members of the old rebel groups, she was a founder of the reborn human race on the Earth. She had found a home, a purpose and a family that she had never known before, nor would ever have been able to know on Gallifrey.

Her path intersected that of the Doctor only once after this. Twenty years after being left on the ruined Earth, she was to take a part in the machinations of Borusa (*The Five Doctors*), and her short reunion with her grandfather at this time remains the last known reference to her adventures. We can only conjecture that she remained on the Earth for the rest of her life.

Romana and the fourth Doctor (*The Ribos Operation*).

CHAPTER 8:

ROMANA

> **'Doctor, sometimes I don't think you're quite right in the head.'**
>
> ROMANA, *THE POWER OF KROLL*

Romanadvoratrelundar was a young – at 140, barely into her second century! – Time Lord freshly graduated from the Academy. She had achieved a triple First – no mean feat – and was definitely feeling full of herself. She was clearly from an ancient and wealthy family – her 70th birthday present was an aircar. Though she took a number of practical courses for her various degrees, she also took some questionable ones. Deciding to forgo 'Veteran And Vintage Vehicles' (including the Type 40), for example, she took a course on 'The Lifestyle Of The Gallifreyan Flutterwing.'

During her period of studies, she worked for a while in the Bureau of Ancient Records. Whilst working on her thesis, she was apparently contacted by the President of the Supreme Council, Borusa, and assigned to help the Doctor in his quest to find the Key to Time (see Chapter 16). In fact, it had been the disguised White Guardian who had enrolled her, knowing that she would prove to be of invaluable help to the Doctor.

Her main failing was that she was filled with purely academic learning. She had no travel experiences, and no practical knowledge of other worlds. Though she stumbled frequently, she proved adaptable and intelligent enough to survive and to grow. Not used at all to dealing with living creatures, her first encounter with a horse, for example, left her wondering how to start it. The period of time she spent with the Doctor broadened her experiences considerably. Her near-photographic memory and attention to details helped her greatly.

From the start, though, she had proven to be a very shrewd judge of the Doctor's character. When he refused to allow her to help, she bullied him into taking her along, and skilfully manipulated his ego to force him to prove his abilities to her. Fond of psychology, she practised it on him as often as it was possible, often wrapping him about her little finger and leaving him somewhat bewildered. She was also a serious student of sociology, and was fond of showing off her learning in this field.

She had a very strong love of clothing and jewellery, and loved dressing up. Unfortunately, due to her lack of practical experience, she frequently selected highly inappropriate outfits for her needs (as in *The Stones of Blood*). As she progressed, though, her costumes became more practical, if never any less garish and eye-catching.

As a Time Lord, she was very filled with her own self-importance, and this often manifested itself as arrogance with beings that she considered to be inferior to herself. She could verbally whip them into

STORIES:
(1) The Ribos Operation
The Pirate Planet
The Stones Of Blood
The Androids Of Tara
The Power Of Kroll
The Armageddon Factor
(2) Destiny Of The Daleks
City Of Death
The Creature From The Pit
Nightmare Of Eden
The Horns Of Nimon
Shada (unshown)
The Leisure Hive
Meglos
Full Circle
State Of Decay
Warriors' Gate
The Five Doctors
(clips from *Shada* only)

Romana first appeared in *The Ribos Operation.*

The fourth Doctor and Romana with Princess Astra, on whom Romana based her regeneration.

line, and managed to take command of situations simply through imposing her will on others. Again, as she spent time with the Doctor, the edges were knocked off her arrogant attitudes and she began to see that each person had his, her or its own worth. The pride she felt in the Time Lords began to erode from unquestioned superiority and turned into a desire to help others who were not as fortunate as herself.

She preferred to work according to the book – understandably, since she had never known any other way of dealing with life. This often clashed with the Doctor's brash, off-the-cuff approach to life. She would look up in the gazetteer worlds that they were planning to visit, while he would know all about them without apparently needing to check. She would attempt to fly the TARDIS according to the manual (*The Pirate Planet*); he would tear out the pages as being utter garbage. With time, she began to see that the Doctor's methods were the result of his 523 years of travels, and that he really did know what he was doing – most of the time.

Together, the two of them managed to collect the first five segments of the Key to Time. The first section was disguised as a piece of Jethrik, one of the rarest and most valuable elements in the Universe. Used by the con-man Garron and his accomplice, Unstoffe, in a complex scam played on the homicidal Graff Vynda-K, the Doctor and Romana had a great deal of difficulty in getting hold of the 'Jethrik'. In the course of the adventure, Romana ran into a Shriven-

zale – a ferocious animal used to guard the jewels of the planet Ribos. Used to the sedentary life of Gallifrey and its harmless wildlife, she was stunned by this savage beast. She queried the Doctor about it, wondering if there were many such animals on other worlds. His reply of 'lots' did little to comfort her.

The second segment turned out to be the entire planet of Callufrax. To obtain this segment, she and the Doctor had to confront the Captain of the Pirate Planet, Zanak, and its mad, senile Queen, Xanxia. Romana had also developed a skill at picking the Doctor's pocket for his jelly babies by this point. With the help of the telepathic gestalt of the Mentiads, the Doctor and Romana stopped the Captain's insane attempts to raid and destroy other worlds.

The third segment was found on the Earth. Romana made friends with Professor Rumford, an eccentric but amiable elderly historian. She was also almost lured to her death by a person using the shapeshifting abilities of the segment to impersonate the Doctor. Eventually, the culprit turned out to be an alien criminal, Cessair of Diplos. With the aid of the silicon-based Ogri, Cessair had fled justice, but was eventually sealed up eternally as a stone.

By this time, the Doctor was getting bored, and he sent Romana off alone after the fourth segment, located on the planet Tara. Romana was captured by Count Grendel, and used as a pawn in his complex attempt to gain the throne of Tara. It turned out that Romana was an exact double of the Princess Strella,

The second Romana with K-9, the Doctor's robot dog (*Shada*).

second in line for the throne. The Doctor fell into the company of the first in line, Prince Reynart. Romana had become quite good at picking locks, and effected a temporary escape. Finally, she and the Doctor saved Reynart and Strella, and Grendel fled into exile.

The fifth segment had accidentally been swallowed by a giant squid-like creature on one of the moons of Delta Magna. It had then grown to immense proportions, which the native Swampies viewed as a god. They attempted to offer up Romana as a sacrifice to it, but she and the Doctor stumbled into a plot by Thawn, the mining engineer of a methane plant, to wipe out the Swampies. The Doctor deduced what the power of Kroll was, and managed to get it to revert to tiny form when he recovered the segment.

In the process of locating the sixth segment, Romana was captured by the Shadow. An agent of the Black Guardian, the Shadow preferred direct and unsubtle methods of getting his information, and accordingly tortured Romana to get what he wanted from her. The Doctor rescued her and together they defeated the Shadow. Presumably because her body had been seriously damaged by the torture inflicted on her, Romana was forced to regenerate.

Since this was her first regeneration and she was still so young, she had a great degree of control over the change. She was able to 'design' her new form to be a duplicate of that of the Princess Astra of Atrios, the living being whose body had been the hidden sixth segment of the Key to Time. Though the Doctor didn't approve of her borrowing the appearance of another person, he finally allowed her her choice. As with all regenerations, Romana's brought on something of a change in personality as well.

She became a little more frivolous, even a little impish. She still retained much of her previous traits, however, including a love of strange clothing, an imperious nature and a quirky way of dealing with the Doctor. Ultimately, the Time Lords discovered that she had left Gallifrey without proper authorization (the mission for a Guardian apparently not being considered 'authorized'), and the Doctor was ordered to return her home (*Full Circle*). By this time, however, Romana was a very changed person. She had realized through her travels that her old life on Gallifrey had been narrow, unfulfilled and boring. She did not want to return home. Though the Doctor sympathized with her problem, he had very little choice but to obey the Time Lords.

However, before he could do this, the TARDIS accidentally passed through a CVE (Charged Vacuum Emboitment) that took it out of normal space (N-space) into E-space, a smaller, separate Universe. Without knowing the way home, neither of them could do much about the summons to Gallifrey. In E-space, they landed on the planet Alzarius, which had the same coordinates as Gallifrey in our Universe.

The Doctor and Romana encountered a creature from the legends of Gallifrey when they next chanced on a small world in E-space. Here, the Great Vampire had been sleeping, recovering from the wounds inflicted upon it by the Time Lords aeons before. Realizing that Romana was a Time Lord, the Three Lords of the world – vampires themselves – determined to sacrifice her to the Great Vampire on its arising. The Doctor managed to stake the vampire and save Romana's life.

Still searching for the exit from E-Space, the TARDIS was affected by the time winds, and came to rest close by the Gateway at the junction of the two Universes. Romana was captured by Rorvik and his crew, whose time-travelling ship had also become stuck there. She and the Doctor discovered that the ship was transporting a load of slaves – the time-sensitive Tharils. Once the masters of most of space, the Tharils had been defeated by the Gundan robots, and then enslaved themselves. Now, however, was the dawn of their freedom. Having learned from their humbling fate, the Tharils were a much-changed race. The Doctor and Romana aided Biroc and Lazlo in freeing their trapped people from the slave ship. While the time winds opened the passageway to return to our normal Universe, the Doctor and Adric alone returned.

Romana had elected to stay behind and to help the Tharils to trace and free the remnant of their people. The Doctor left K9 with her, and he contained all the information needed for her to build another TARDIS that could operate in E-Space. With no regrets, Romana turned her back on her own people and normal space, to stay and aid where she was most needed. It was a tremendous change from the Romana who had initially stepped into the TARDIS with the Doctor – but, as with most of his companions, the Doctor had proved most influential in shaping her life.

CHAPTER 9:

RASSILON

The history of Rassilon is very contradictory, but is generally laid out in *The Book of the Old Time*. The Old Time is what the Time Lords call the pre-Time Lord days of Gallifrey, when the Gallifreyans relied on simple technology such as Transmats, and is now many thousands of years in the past. The Time Lords have, ironically, lost much knowledge of their own past. They spend much time investigating the lifelines of other worlds, and have neglected their own.

Rassilon did not invent the power of time travel. Before he came to power, the Gallifreyans already possessed some ability to manipulate time. This was a period of unrest in the history of the planet, and this power was not put to good use. The Time Scoop had probably been invented with a noble intention in mind – taking objects from out of the past and bringing them into the present. It would have been an excellent tool for archaeological study, for example, but was put to a twisted use: the Games.

The Gallifreyans would use the Time Scoop to snatch people and aliens from their own past or those of other worlds and then place them within the Death Zone. This bleak, unfriendly area of Gallifrey is ringed in with mountains, but to make it impossible for the 'contestants' to escape, the extra security of a force field was added. The Players in the Game were then forced to fight each other to the death for the pleasure of the jaded Gallifreyans who watched the events on their Public Access Channels. Only two races were never 'invited' to compete in the Games – the Daleks and the Cybermen, both of whom were too deadly (and boring, since they killed without pleasure) to be allowed to play.

> **'Rassilon – the single greatest figure in Time Lord history.'**
>
> THE SECOND DOCTOR,
> *THE FIVE DOCTORS*

> **STORY:**
> *The Five Doctors*

When Rassilon came to power, he forbade the Games, sealed off the Death Zone and locked away the controls of the Time Scoop. Their location was recorded only in the forbidden *Black Scrolls of Rassilon*. It was then made a capital offence either to read the *Scrolls* or to use the Time Scoop and Death Zone.

Even at this point in his life, Rassilon was planning far ahead. Any other being would have destroyed both the Scoop and all knowledge of it. He, however, foresaw a great need for the forbidden knowledge.

Rassilon, according to *The Book of the Old Time,* was originally an engineer and an architect. He worked with Omega to create the power of the Eye of Harmony. Rassilon entered a black hole, engineered by Omega, with a fleet of ships, stabilizing the core of the black hole, and returning it to Gallifrey in power restrainers. The Sash of Rassilon was a technological shield that enabled Rassilon to withstand the tremendous energy bursts and vast forces about the core, and he harnessed the power into the Eye of Harmony. All of the Time Lords' power now comes from the 'tamed' black hole. It is maintained beneath the Panopticon, and can only be accessed using the Great Key.

Rassilon is also credited with creating the Transduction Barriers that surround Gallifrey, keeping it secure from alien attack. In fact, he may not have created these force shields but simply commissioned them. Still, since his specialty was in force field manipulation, it remains probable that they were, indeed, one of his own inventions.

Rassilon planned in the long term for his race.

Though the Lord President is given the Sash of Rassilon and the Rod of Rassilon, the President has never been given the Great Key. Rassilon deliberately passed knowledge of the Key to the Chancellors instead of the President. Without the Key, no President could thus become the absolute ruler of the Time Lords and create a dictatorship.

Rassilon also created the ultimate weapon for the Time Lords, but one that he deemed too dangerous to use – the Demat Gun. Knowledge of its existence is kept within the Matrix, but the Great Key of Rassilon is needed to construct and power the Gun. Though the President may know of the device, he cannot operate it without the Key – which no President before the Doctor has ever held.

Apparently the Demat Gun works like a simple disintegrator, but it is far more complex than that. It

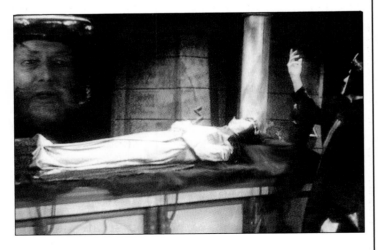

Rasillon as he appeared in his tomb (*The Five Doctors*).

need not be focused on a visible target, but can be hooked in to any time controls and used as a weapon to destroy anyone or anything in the reaches of time and space. Knowing the dangers of such a weapon falling into the wrong hands, Rassilon had the knowledge of how to build it carefully hidden. It has in fact been built and operated only once to anyone's knowledge – by the Doctor during the Sontaran *Invasion of Time.*

Rassilon's final fate is not accurately known. Though he is considered by most to be a figure of great good, there are dark rumours to the contrary. How exactly he came to power is not known, but it was almost certainly not without bloodshed. Though his reforms changed forever the society of Gallifrey, and he created almost single-handed the civilization, laws and ethics of the Time Lords, he had his darker side. Stories circulated that he was a cruel despot, killing all of his foes, and ruthlessly subjugating the Gallifreyans to his will. Naturally, few such stories ever made it into any kind of official history. *The Book of the Old Time,* written by an unknown Time Lord, naturally records this period from Rassilon's point of view – and any winner in a bloody struggle inevitably paints himself in the best light.

Whether Rassilon was a saint or a devil is hard to judge. He was, in all probability, a person with many aspects. However, his final moments have never been played out. A portion of his mind and knowledge resides within the Matrix – probably severely edited, since much of the truth about him has been lost. Certainly he never intended the future Presidents of the Time Lords to have access to everything that he himself knew. The Demat Gun and the Time Scoop were both hidden by him, and the knowledge about them virtually erased.

One of the stories about him reports that in the end the Time Lords rebelled against him on account of his cruelty, and then locked him in the Black Tower in the heart of the Death Zone. There he was reported to live on in eternal sleep. The Tower was certainly known as the Tomb of Rassilon, and its image was familiar to generations of Time Lords – an imposing building with a horned summit and three entrances. It is so well known that a children's nursery rhyme was made up about it. However, very few people have ever visited it, and of those who have, far fewer have ever returned.

Rassilon's ever-devious mind laid a trap, however.

The Raston robot confronts Cybermen in the Death Zone on Gallifrey (*The Five Doctors*).

Though Time Lords are very long-lived, they are not truly immortal. Rassilon left a trail claiming that he had discovered the secret of true immortality, and that it might be gained by anyone who would venture into the Death Zone and switch off the force field that guarded it. Despite the apparent foolishness of the tale, Rassilon knew full well that it would lure the greedy and unscrupulous into the Zone.

Over the millennia, four Time Lords have made it through the Death Zone to the Tomb. The names of the first three are lost in the mists of time, but the fourth was Borusa (Chapter 13). He claimed his prize after forcing the various incarnations of the Doctor to do the hard and dangerous part of the work for him – penetrating the Death Zone. But the prize of immortality had its price – Borusa followed the others into the immortality of living stone. His reward was to suffer endless regret for his actions.

Rassilon had laid the trap to remove potential dictators from the Time Lord race. His mind controls the Dark Tower, though whether he is still alive somehow, or whether this Tower is host to some complex mechanical mind such as the Matrix is uncertain. When the Doctors had arrived there, they were confronted by a reasoning facsimile of Rassilon. It was clearly a projection of some kind, but of what type is uncertain. Perhaps Rassilon does rest in his Tomb in unending sleep, and this was a form of mental projection, such as the waves of fear his mind sent through the Doctor's companions. Or perhaps it is merely some mechanical projection programmed long before, and lasting almost eternally.

How Rassilon could accomplish the feats of turning a living being into stone is unclear. However, it must be recalled that his speciality was in the construction of force fields, so perhaps he has merely discovered a

The servants of the Great Vampire prepare to sacrifice Romana (*State of Decay*).

method for preserving living beings in a stasis that resembles stone. Rassilon also had the ability to move persons and objects through time from this Tomb, though it is probable that he may have been tapping into the Eye of Harmony to do so. Clearly, the full extent of Rassilon's abilities have not yet been revealed.

What was most interesting about the Doctor's encounter with Rassilon is the fact that Rassilon could address him by name without having asked it. Was this no more than mind-reading – or had the two of them met while Rassilon was still alive? The seventh Doctor (*Remembrance of the Daleks*) hinted that he and Rassilon worked together at one time...

During the time of Rassilon, the Universe was invaded by an army of Giant Vampires. These creatures were so powerful that a single one of them could drain the life from an entire planet. The Time Lords fought back against the monsters, and after a terrible and bloody war, they destroyed all but the King Vampire, which vanished. The only method of killing the vampires proved to be to destroy their hearts. To achieve this, the Time Lords built Bowships, which launched gigantic steel bolts to pierce the vampires. They believed that all were destroyed, but just in case the one missing vampire turned up, all Type 40 Time Vehicles were mandated to carry 'The Record of Rassilon', which told of the war, and insisted that any surviving vampire must be dealt with immediately.

The missing King Vampire had escaped the slaughter accidentally, falling through a CVE (Charged Vacuum Emboitment) into E-Space, a small Universe independent of our own. The Doctor and Romana encountered this creature and its minions (*State of Decay*). They managed to destroy it before it could recover from its wounds and return to our Universe to begin its bloody wars over again.

So devastating had the war with the vampires proved that the Time Lords became avowed pacifists thereafter.

CHAPTER 10:

OMEGA

Omega was the stellar engineer who created the power supply that enabled the Time Lords to start up their time travel facility. A large sun was selected to be tapped for the energy demands of the Time Lords, and Omega and his team went to work. He triggered a supernova explosion, which was then converted into a white hole, tied to the power taps on Gallifrey. In the process, Omega's ship was destroyed, and it was presumed that Omega was lost with it.

In fact, he was still alive. The forces unleashed in the conversion process had propelled him through the white hole and into a separate Universe beyond. This was a universe composed entirely of anti-matter, yet somehow, through the sheer force of his will, Omega managed to survive. The connecting point between the two universes was the point of Singularity. This point Omega finally bent to his own will, and he used the power of the Singularity to create an entire world for himself, and a palace on that world in which to dwell.

He was unable to create complex life forms, and for thousands of years he remained the only inhabitant of this universe. Lonely and bitter, he brooded on his fate, and became convinced that he had been deliberately abandoned by the Time Lords, who saw his engineering abilities as a threat to themselves. (There may, in fact, be some truth in his suspicions.) He became determined to have his revenge on them.

However, Omega was unable to leave this pocket universe of his without some other mind present to take it over. Experimenting with the Singularity, however, he found that he had greater powers than he had ever imagined. The flow of power from the white hole to Gallifrey was reversible, and he began to drain the energy of the Time Lords. Initially, this was a slow process, but it soon built up momentum. He would be able to gain his revenge by destroying

STORIES:
(1) The Three Doctors
(2) Arc of Infinity

The first appearance of Omega (*The Three Doctors*).

Gallifrey – if there was no intervention. He had also tapped into the information network, and found out about the exile of the Doctor on the Earth.

He managed to send a bolt of 'lightning' to Earth, drawing the attention of the third Doctor. Using the beam, he then sent one of his primitive life forms to Earth to capture the Doctor. The Time Lords were helpless to intervene directly, but were able to bring two earlier incarnations of the Doctor forward in their time lines to help the third Doctor.

The second and third Doctors faced Omega in his anti-matter Universe, where they heard his tale. Omega wanted his freedom, but the Doctors discovered that the corrosive nature of the Singularity had in fact destroyed everything of Omega but his will. It was impossible for him ever to leave his universe and still live. Close to madness to begin with, this information tipped Omega completely over the edge. The

The second and third Doctors in Omega's anti-matter world (*The Three Doctors*).

Doctors managed to defeat his plans and to lay Omega to rest in the only way open to him: death. Using a small piece of matter (the second Doctor's recorder, unchanged by passage into the anti-matter universe), the Doctors destroyed all of the pocket universe, and Omega along with it – or so they thought.

But Omega was not dead; his will still kept him alive. His original doorway to the matter Universe that we inhabit had been destroyed, but he discovered another – the Arc of Infinity. The Arc is a region of space/time in the vicinity of a collapsed Q star. It is essentially a wide band of quantum magnetism that can keep matter and anti-matter separate. Omega could thus stabilize himself, and once again restore his contacts with the Universe of matter.

The Arc varied through time and space, impacting on many regions and worlds. Once again, Omega's indomitable will bent the physical universe to his control, and he managed to make the Arc project itself wherever he willed. One portion passed through the region of space where Gallifrey exists. Using this, Omega managed to contact Hedin, a Time Lord on the High Council. Hedin, impelled by a false sense of loyalty to what Omega once was, agreed to help the renegade to re-enter normal space and time.

This could be done only if Omega could be provided with the body print of a Time Lord, so that Omega could then fuse his mind with the physical portion of that Time Lord. Hedin selected the bio scan data of the Doctor for this – a decision that Omega found particularly appropriate. However, Hedin's transmission of the data was intercepted, and the High Council alerted to the threat. Omega had managed to enter the Matrix, and seized some control of it. Terrified lest he gain further control, the Council panicked, and decided that the simplest and fastest way of getting rid of the invader was to destroy the Doctor – the body that the intruder wished to meld with.

The Doctor's TARDIS was dragged back to Gallifrey, and the Doctor sentenced to death. Omega had, however, been expecting this, and his pawn, Hedin, programmed the termination machinery to cut out at the crucial moment. The Doctor was kept alive, and he managed to discern that Omega was hiding on another familiar planet – Earth. Through Hedin's intervention, Omega had gained control of a TARDIS, and he had also created a matter being, the Ergon, to do his will. The Doctor, aided by his companion Nyssa

The first, third and second Doctors (*The Three Doctors*).

The second Doctor captured by Gell Guards (*The Three Doctors*).

and a technician named Damon, tracked down Omega.

The Doctor shorted out the transfer, condemning Omega to return to the anti-matter Universe he inhabited. Since the transfer of data had almost been accomplished, though, Omega took a wild chance and remained in the matter Universe. Sadly, his control began to deteriorate, and the Doctor was forced to annihilate him in order to prevent a massive explosion when he reverted to his anti-matter form.

But can we be certain that Omega has been destroyed?

In *Remembrance of the Daleks,* we were told that Omega created the supernova using a stellar manipulator that he named the 'Hand of Omega'. The Doctor and Rassilon had aided in its construction. After the device was used, the Doctor stole the only other existing version of the Hand, hiding it on the Earth. When the Daleks sought it out, the Doctor

used it to destroy Skaro, their home world – although we should not assume that the Daleks were entirely wiped out.

In *Silver Nemesis,* we learned that Omega created the living metal validium as the final defence for the planet Gallifrey. The leftovers somehow found their way to Earth, where Lady Peinforte forged it into a statue of herself, which she named Nemesis. Somehow its influence increases evil tendencies in people – it drove her insane. The Doctor launched it into space, but its baleful influence every 25 years created problems for Earth. It finally impacted on the Earth in 1988, when it was sought by the Cybermen, among others. The Doctor used Nemesis to destroy the Cyberman fleet, and then sent it off once again into the depths of space.

During the course of this story, the Doctor is revealed by Lady Peinforte as being 'from the time of chaos' on Gallifrey.

Nyssa, President Borusa and the fifth Doctor held at gunpoint by Hedin (*Arc of Infinity*).

Inset: Omega's appearance before the transformation.

Omega adopted the appearance of the fifth Doctor in *Arc of Infinity*.

The Monk (*The Time Meddler*).

CHAPTER 11:

THE MONK

The first time that we were introduced to anyone from the Doctor's home world – aside from his granddaughter – was when the Monk's trail of interference was discovered on an English beach in AD 1066. As the tale unfolded, it was clear that though the Monk and the Doctor had never previously met, they were both of the same race – though just what race was never mentioned, nor was the name of their home world.

Like the Doctor, the Monk had stolen a TARDIS and disappeared into the space-time Vortex, untraced by the Time Lords. In his case, however, the Monk had taken a fully-functional model, of a more advanced design than that of the Doctor. This suggested that he had left at a later date, though obviously long before the Doctor gained any notoriety among the Time Lords. The Monk had very different aims from the Doctor in his travels. Like the Doctor, he disliked the Time Lord policy of non-interference, but unlike the Doctor, the Monk was not interested in intervening in the affairs of planets for good. And, unlike the Master, he was not interested either in pure evil or in furthering his own ends.

What motivated the Monk was the fact that he had the power to interfere. In something of an experimental mood, his aim was to change the course of history because he thought he could order it better. His plan was to destroy the attacking fleet of Norman ships and thus change the history of England. This was not out of any real love for Harold and his reign, but simply to see if he really could manage to do it.

The Doctor was firmly opposed to such meddling, and managed to defeat the Monk, stranding him on the Earth and stealing the key component of his TARDIS's interior dimensional controls.

> **STORIES:**
> *The Time Meddler*
> *The Daleks'*
> *Masterplan*

The Monk was rather annoyed at this, but not defeated. Despite his somewhat bumbling manner, the Monk was actually quite a fine scientist in his own right, and he managed to substitute a laser combination for the missing component and regain the use of his ship. His first thought was of revenge.

He managed to track down the Doctor on the volcanic planet Tigus. Using his knowledge of light, he managed to seal the TARDIS lock, hoping to strand the Doctor for a while. Though he wanted revenge, the Monk was not sadistic enough to strand the Doctor and his companions forever. However, the Doctor managed to break through the tinkered lock and leave Tigus. Thoroughly annoyed now, the Monk gave chase.

Realizing that the Doctor would be on the alert, the Monk jumped time tracks – a difficult and even dangerous trick, but one which meant that he could not be traced. He emerged to find himself in Pharonic Egypt, and embedded in the midst of a fight between the Doctor and the Daleks.

Self-preservation being one of his stronger points, the Monk realized that this game was getting too much for him now. He wanted to get his own back on the Doctor, but not at the risk of his own life. Through a bit of fast talking and switching sides whenever the opportunity arose, the Monk managed to dance about on the edge of extermination. Finally, he bolted for his TARDIS and left as fast as he could only to discover that the Doctor had stolen his directional unit. He was now left adrift in the Vortex, wandering as aimlessly as the Doctor's TARDIS ever had.

So far, nothing more has been heard of the Monk, but his path and the Doctor's will undoubtedly intersect again some time in the future – or the past. The Monk is neither evil nor malicious – he is more like a petulant child, spoilt, and wanting his own way. Lacking self-discipline, he interferes simply for the fun of it. In many ways, his lack of foresight and completely oblivious foolishness can make him more dangerous than foes who are actively aggressive. He seems incapable of appreciating the results of his efforts to change time, and is almost unreachable by any form of logic.

CHAPTER 12:

THE MASTER

The Master is in many ways the antithesis of the Doctor. Where the Doctor cares about other beings and cultures, the Master lives only to gratify his own desires. He views the Doctor's compassion as his 'fatal weakness', and he shares none of it. As a result, he is perhaps the greatest mass murderer of all of time and space. Among the victims of his schemes are the inhabitants of Atlantis (*The Time Monster*) and several entire worlds he wiped from being (*Logopolis*). To him, individual lives (provided they belong to others) are worthless, and he ruthlessly kills and enslaves to achieve his own ends.

> **'That jackanapes! All he ever does is cause trouble!'**
>
> THE DOCTOR, *TERROR OF THE AUTONS*
>
> **'A Cosmos without the Doctor scarcely bears thinking about.'**
>
> THE MASTER, *THE FIVE DOCTORS*

The Master is a skilled mathematician, and a graduate of the Prydon Academy. He has a degree in Cosmic Science that is better than the Doctor's own. His one failing, according to the Rani and others, is a thirst for revenge that knows no rational boundaries. 'Vanity is his weakness', the Doctor claims. One aspect of this vanity is that the identities he selects to hide behind are variations on his name – in *The Daemons*, he poses as Magister, and in *The Time Monster* as Thascales – both of which are classical versions of the word 'master'.

Both the Master and the Doctor attended the Academy at the same time, and both formed ideas about leaving Gallifrey. Susan (*The Five Doctors*) didn't recognize him, so we may assume that they were not well acquainted in those days. This soon changed. Somehow, the Doctor ran afoul of the Master, who then vowed to kill him. Since the Master had been imprisoned on Gallifrey, it seems logical that in some manner the Doctor had been responsible for his capture.

Unlike the Doctor, the Master's passion was for power. Delighting in deviousness and trickery, he stole most of his ideas from other people and beings (as in *Time Flight*). When the Doctor took a TARDIS and left Gallifrey, he inspired the Master to make his own ambitions plain. He, too, stole a TARDIS, and began to create trouble in the Universe. Knowing that the Doctor had been exiled on the Earth, the Master followed him there and when his escape was detected by the Time Lords, they easily deduced that he had headed for the Earth. The Tribunal that had sentenced the Doctor to exile on the Earth now sent one of their members to warn the Doctor. Though the Doctor characterized the Master as 'an unimaginative plodder', the Master was far more than this. As the Time Lord informed the Doctor: 'He's learned a lot since you last met him.'

The Master had indeed. Along with a more sophisticated TARDIS, the Master also possessed a portable matter compactor, the Tissue Compression Eliminator, which can shrink

STORIES:

(1) *Terror Of The Autons*
The Mind Of Evil
Claws Of Axos
Colony In Space
The Daemons
The Sea Devils
The Time Monster
Frontier In Space
(2) *The Deadly Assassin*
(3) *The Keeper Of Traken*
(4) *The Keeper Of Traken*
Logopolis
Castrovalva
Time Flight
The King's Demons
The Five Doctors
Planet Of Fire
The Caves Of Androzani
Mark Of The Rani
The Ultimate Foe
Survival

The Master as he first appeared (*Terror of the Autons*).

The third Doctor explaining to UNIT troops that the Master has escaped (*The Terror of the Autons*).

living beings in size and kill them. Over the years, this characteristic method of killing has become something of a calling card for him. Like so much else, this presumably was stolen from some alien race. The Master had somehow linked with the Nestene Consciousness, and learned of its past failure to invade the Earth successfully. Liking the idea of wiping out the Doctor's favourite race, the Master agreed to help the Nestenes in another attempt to conquer the Earth.

Using his powers of hypnosis, the Master seized control of Farrel Plastics. With the aid of mesmerized minions, he stole the last remaining Nestene Energy Unit and revitalized it. With reconstructed Autons – plastic forms animated by a Nestene – he sought to bring the Nestene Consciousness to the Earth using a radio telescope. However, in assuming that the Nestenes would be grateful the Master had badly miscalculated. The Doctor made him realize that the Nestenes would kill him also, and the two adversaries worked together to send the Consciousness back into the depths of space and end the invasion.

This inability of the Master's to realize when he had gone too far in his plans would continue to plague him down the years. He often aided the wrong side in a struggle (as in *The Sea Devils* or *The Claws of Axos*) simply out of a desire for revenge against either the Doctor or the human race.

The Master's other great ability – creating flawless disguises – now helped him to escape the Doctor and the forces of UNIT. Rex Farrel died in the Master's place, while the renegade Time Lord escaped to fight again. However, the Doctor had removed the dematerialization circuit from the Master's TARDIS, trapping him on the Earth. Though an international dragnet was set up, the Master managed to avoid it.

When he turned up again, he was disguised as the scientist behind the Keller Machine, supposedly designed to extract the evil from within a man's mind. In fact, the Keller Machine housed an alien parasite that the Master had stumbled on during one of his trips. At the same time, the Master used the inmates of Stangmoor Prison to help in his attempts to sabotage a peace conference vital to the world. Once again, the Doctor managed to interfere with the Master's plans, and destroyed the alien parasite before it could grow uncontrollable.

Attempting to escape from the Earth, the Master then arrived on the living ship/being known as Axos, a shape-shifting energy vampire. Attempting to regain his own freedom, the Master led Axos to the Earth. Posing as a benevolent being, Axos managed to fool the political powers into accepting it, but the Doctor had reservations about the aims of the creature. Infiltrating the ship, he met with the Master, and discovered the truth about the intentions of Axos. The Master agreed to help the Doctor to defeat Axos, since it was the only way that he could regain his own freedom. The two Time Lords trapped Axos for ever in a time loop. The Doctor managed to escape from this in his TARDIS, and suspected that the Master may have managed the same feat. Sadly, he proved to be correct.

The Master, masquerading as Professor Thascales, with the Crystal of Kronos (*The Time Monster*).

The Time Lords discovered the loss of the file on the Doomsday Weapon, and realized that only the Master could have taken it. They were forced to use the Doctor in an attempt to recover it, and the Doctor and Jo found themselves on an Earth colony planet in the year AD 2472. The colonists were locked in a war of wits and nerve with the Interplanetary Mining Corporation. IMC wanted the planet for its mineral wealth, and was framing a non-existent monster and the native race for murdering various colonists. An arbitrator from Earth was called in, but it proved to be the Master in another of his disguises.

As ever, the Master convinced everybody – except the Doctor, of course – and charmed them into aiding his own plans to recover the hidden Doomsday Weapon. The Doctor, however, managed to help the colonists in their struggle for freedom. He also persuaded the alien Priest guarding the Doomsday Weapon that it should never be allowed to fall into the wrong hands. The Priest destroyed the Weapon, but once again the Master made his getaway.

Back on Earth, the Master posed as the new clergyman of the church in Devil's End – a small, rural village whose local barrow hid the site of the Daemons, a spacefaring race whose biological experiments include the mutation of the human race. Azal, the Daemon left on the Earth, was to judge the human race as either worthy of receiving the tremendous powers of the Daemons, or as a flawed experiment to be destroyed. The Master tried to convince Azal to hand him the promised powers, but even Azal could see through the Master's greed, and offered the power to the Doctor instead. The Doctor refused him, annoying the Daemon, who was destroyed by a selfless act of bravery by Jo. The Master was captured by the forces of UNIT, and held in a special prison under the charge of Colonel Trenchard.

Trenchard was an old-school type, and susceptible to the Master's ingratiating charm. In the local area, several ships had been lost at sea, and the Master convinced the gullible Trenchard that he could help locate the cause, and make Trenchard a hero. The Master had deduced that the Sea Devils, creatures that had once ruled the Earth in the age of the dinosaurs, were responsible for the sinking of the ships, and the Master convinced them that he wanted to help them to get their old planet back from the human race. The Doctor managed to intervene again, showing the Master's true nature to the Sea Devils. When the Sea Devils were once again sealed in their

The Master at the end of his cycle of regenerations (*The Deadly Assassin*).

tombs by an attack force, the Doctor and the Master both escaped to the surface. Once again, the Master's powers of disguise helped him to escape capture.

Along with his skills as a physical mimic, the Master is also adept at vocal mimicry. He does a very good impression of Brigadier Lethbridge Stewart (*The Time Monster*). The Master has an almost complete disregard for the end results of his plans. More than once he has placed the entire Universe in jeopardy. In *The Time Monster*, he planned to control Kronos, the most dangerous of the Chronovores – creatures that normally exist outside of time, and who can devour particles of time. If loosed within time, such a creature might break down the boundaries of reality and cause everything to dissolve into absolute chaos. In his insane quest for power, the Master was more than willing to risk this happening. Another example of this callous disregard for consequences was in his attempt to seize control of the Universe through the Block Transfer Computations of the Logopolitans (*Logopolis*), resulting in the annihilation of that and several other worlds before the Doctor could stop the breakdown of the physical Universe.

The Master's final confrontation with the Doctor while in his first incarnation (presumably his first; it is never made clear) was over the 'Frontier in Space'. In the near future, both Earth and Draconia have expanded their Empires into space, and stand at an uneasy peace. It would have taken very little to provoke war between the two powers, and a series of border incidents inflamed both sides. Each assumed that the other was attempting to begin a war of conquest – when in fact the true instigator of the problems was the Master. He had been hired by the Daleks to start a war between Earth and Draconia, in order to weaken both empires and leave the Daleks in complete mastery of known space. This plan appealed to the Master's sense of humour (he even read H.G. Wells' *War Of The Worlds* as he worked), and he readily undertook the task. Needing help with the plan – and soldiers to risk their lives – he reluctantly accepted the help of the Ogrons for this task. His arrogance didn't make their relationship an easy one, and in the end the Doctor managed to confuse and defeat the simple-minded Ogrons. The Master fled the scene as his plan became unworkable.

His schemes had caused the Master to work through his regeneration cycle very quickly indeed. His final regeneration proved very short-lived, and his body began to suffer the effects of the stresses he had placed it under. He began to decay physically, but never mentally. Determined to renew his regeneration cycle, he plotted and schemed. Like the Doctor, he was well acquainted with the myths of Old Gallifrey, and he pieced together the truth about the Sash of Rassilon, realizing that with it in his grasp, he could suffuse his body with the power he needed to regenerate once again.

It was almost too late for the Master, who was dying. He arrived on the planet Tersurus, where he met and suborned Goth. Goth agreed to help the Master in order to get back at the President of the Time Lords. Goth, an ambitious man, was already the Chancellor of the Prydonian Chapter, and one of the most powerful men on Gallifrey. He wanted to become the President, but the retiring President saw through Goths façade, and realized that he would be the wrong man for the post. Unwisely, he mentioned this to Goth. When the Master offered his aid, Goth was willing to accept.

Together, they planned the death of the President before he could name his chosen successor, so that an election would have to be held to fill the post – an election Goth was certain to win. In order to provide a culprit, the Master intended to frame the Doctor for the assassination of the President. It would be a stroke of beautiful irony, and would get the Doctor into lethal trouble. Then when Goth assumed the office of President, the Master would have access to the Sash of Rassilon and the Great Key – both of which he would need to control the Eye of Harmony.

The Master was unwittingly helped in his plans by the Celestial Intervention Agency. They had hidden the Doctor's records from the public, and managed to bury them away from the current elite. Since they were so frequently cross-referenced to the Doctor's, the Master's own records were also hidden. Goth, as a member of the High Council, had access to the Data Extracts, and helped the Master to destroy his records, and to subvert the Doctor's.

Using his mathematical skills, the Master covered their tracks, and then tapped into the APC Net, gaining access to the Matrix for Goth. Using the Matrix – basically a vast single mind – he sent a mental summons and a prediction of the impending assassination of the President to the Doctor. Naturally, the Doctor fell for the bait and came to Gallifrey. The Master then set up a decoy staser that would look

The Melkur, the statue that was the Master's TARDIS in *The Keeper of Traken*.

like the murder weapon, and arranged for the Doctor to be holding it when Goth actually shot the President. The Doctor was arrested, as planned, and Goth insisted on a quick trial and execution for him.

The plan began to unravel, however, when the Doctor invoked Article 17 of the Constitution, claiming for himself the right to run for the Presidency. The Doctor then deduced the Master's subversion of the Matrix, and entered it mentally to try to track down the interference. The Master had his pawn, Goth, mentally fight the Doctor inside the Matrix. The Doctor proved to be the stronger, and the Master deliberately allowed Goth to perish when the Doctor won. Faking his own death, the Master managed to be placed in the Morgue next to the dead President. He then took the Sash of Rassilon and attempted to gain control of the Eye of Harmony. The Doctor managed to defeat him, but the Master did gain enough energy from his exposure to the Eye to keep his life force going. He escaped Gallifrey, still seeking the additional regenerations that he needed.

He attempted to recover a new body to use – along

with the energy he needed – by taking over the Keepership of Traken. Since only a person of Traken descent could hold the office, he had to work carefully. In addition, Traken was such a peaceful world that its influence actually trapped and calcified any evil being who landed there – such a trapped entity being known as a Melkur. The Master survived this problem by landing his TARDIS on Traken, but never venturing outside. He used its chameleon circuits to make it look like a calcified living being.

The tender-hearted Trakenites took pity even on the doomed evil beings, and one, Kassia, was assigned to tend to the new Melkur. Instead of calcifying and decaying quickly, this one seemed set to last many years. (Presumably, though, the Master didn't sit about all that time. Using his TARDIS's abilities, he could simply have jumped forward in time inside his ship to the point when he had to act.) The Master had made his selection wisely. Kassia was corrupted by him to act as his agent when her husband, Tremas, was named as the Keeper-elect. Wanting to save him from the honour – or fate – of the Keepership, she fell in with the Master's plans.

The fourth Doctor with Keeper-Elect Tremas, whose body was usurped by the Master (*The Keeper of Traken*).

The Master's appearance after taking possession of Tremas (*Logopolis*).

The Keeper was a being who lived an extended lifetime in communion with the Source, a field of power drawn from all living beings in the Traken Union. He was also trapped by it in a chair, confined within the field of operation of the Source. In keeping with the Master's plans, the old Keeper managed to solicit the help of the Doctor and Adric and brought them to Traken. Kassia was forced to assume the Keepership, and through his link with her, the Master murdered her and, still within his TARDIS, took over the powers of the Keeper. The Doctor he kidnapped, aiming to pick his knowledge for his own records and to steal his body in order to regain his mobility. Adric and Nyssa sabotaged the Source, severing the Master's power, and the Doctor managed to escape his clutches and establish a new Keeper.

The Master survived the ordeal, however, and had gained enough energy from his contact with the Source to steal a new body. He took over the form of Tremas, one of the Consuls, and was now endowed with fresh vitality, though not with a new cycle of regenerations.

In his contact with the Doctor, the Master discovered that the Doctor planned to go on to Logopolis. The Master realized that this would suit his own plans, and anticipated the Doctor's moves. The Doctor was aiming to reconfigure the TARDIS's chameleon circuits using the Block Transfer Computations of the Logopolitan mathematicians. This is a system of changing reality through the advanced application of pure mathematics. First, though, the Doctor aimed to measure the exterior dimensions of a real police box.

Knowing this, the Master materialized his own TARDIS about the target police box, so that when the Doctor did the same thing, he brought the Master's TARDIS inside of his own. In order to avoid discovery, the Master killed a policeman, and also Tegan's Aunt Vanessa, and when the Doctor took off for Logopolis, the Master's TARDIS was carried along, arriving undetected by the Logopolitans. He slew one of the mathematicians of Logopolis, and injected incorrect figures into their computations. This resulted in the TARDIS's exterior dimensions shrinking, almost killing the Doctor before corrections could be made.

This, however, was mostly a sideline of the Master's. His real aim was to steal the results of some very secretive research carried out by the Logopolitans.

Blindly unaware of what he was doing, he nullified the calculations of Logopolis. The entire planet began to crumble, and the Monitor – leader of the Logopolitans – revealed that it was only the mathematics of Logopolis that had held back entropy. According to the Second Law Of Thermodynamics, in a closed system, chaos will increase and eventually the Universe will end in what is termed Heat Death – all will be uniformity, and chaos will have won.

The Logopolitans had deduced that the Universe had passed this critical point a long time before, and they had staved off the inevitable by creating the CVEs (Charged Vacuum Emboitments). These were gateways to other Universes, through which entropy had been bled from our own Universe. The Master's foolish actions had closed the CVEs, and now entropy had begun to ravage everything, condemning the Universe to doom.

Reluctantly, the Doctor had been left no choice but to join forces with the Master to combat this. The Logopolitans had almost perfected a programme that would allow the CVEs to stabilize and thus keep the Universe whole, but it had to be run through the Pharos Project computers on Earth. The Doctor and the Master together managed this, though the Master made one last attempt to blackmail the peoples of the Universe into accepting him as their ruler first. The Doctor put a stop to this, but in so doing fell to his death and was forced to regenerate.

(Note: this problem with entropy seems very similar to the earlier problem that the Doctor had faced with the Guardians concerning the Key To Time. Perhaps this solution here finally settled the problem of chaos with the Guardians?)

As the Doctor regenerated, the Master seized his chance and captured Adric. Using the boy's genius for mathematics, the Master set two traps for the Doctor. First, he had a projection of Adric programme the TARDIS to return in time to Event One, the creation of the Galaxy from an inrush of hydrogen – an explosion powerful enough to destroy even a TARDIS. The Doctor managed to avoid this fate by jettisoning parts of the TARDIS and using the mass as a power boost to break free. Then the Master sprang his second, more ingenious trap.

He had adapted the possibilities of Block Transfer Computation and allied them with Adric's powers to create an imaginary city, the Dwellings of Simplicity

The fourth Doctor and the Master joined forces to prevent the destruction of the universe (*Logopolis*)

– Castrovalva. This became real through the powers of the mathematics involved, although it needed to be sustained by the power coming from Hadron power lines, in the midst of which Adric was kept suspended and tortured. The Master then peopled his city with citizens possessing both individuality, charm and goodness – not exactly his trademarks. It is astounding, in many ways, that the Master could have created such gentle, sympathetic people, and seems to prove that somewhere inside, he does understand something of the better side of human and Time Lord natures. Alongside Shardovan the librarian, Mergrave the physician and Ruther, the Master had a role for himself as the Portreeve, the kindly old man who ruled Castrovalva.

The Doctor managed to regain his strength, and began to realize that the place was not what it seemed. It was actually space folded in upon itself, and when the Doctor began to grasp this, he discovered that Castrovalva's dimensions were very bizarre indeed. Shardovan gave his life to free Adric from the

web of Hadron power lines, and this precipitated the collapse of Castrovalva. The Doctor and his friends escaped, but Mergrave and his fellow citizens held the Master back as the dimensions collapsed about him.

Somehow, though, the Master managed to survive this, and escaped once again in his TARDIS which, low on power, stranded him in the prehistoric past of the Earth, one hundred and forty million years ago. Here, in a strange pyramid, he discovered the remains of the Xeraphin, an alien race possessed of amazing powers to change matter. Attempting to break into the pyramid in order to seize the power source he needed, the Master cannibalized his TARDIS to make a time tunnel into the future and to bring back slaves he could hypnotize into doing the manual labour for him. He succeeded in capturing two Concordes in flight, and in bringing them into the past. On the second, however, were the Doctor and his friends, who were investigating the vanishing of the first.

The Master had disguised himself as the ugly Kalid, but was eventually unmasked. He attempted to power up his TARDIS again by stealing parts from the Doctor's TARDIS, but without a great deal of success. The Doctor managed to return the stolen people to their correct time, and he sent the Master's TARDIS to Xeriphas, where the imprisoned Xeraphin would finally be able to free themselves. The Doctor rather hoped that the Master would be stuck there, but instead he managed yet again to power up his TARDIS and to escape – this time taking with him Kamelion.

Kamelion was the tool of a former invader of Xeriphas, a sophisticated robot capable of assuming infinite forms and personalities. Though Kamelion possessed a mind of its own, this true personality was submerged while it was under the control of another being. The Master planned to use Kamelion's powers to create chaos throughout the Universe. He began by arriving on Earth in March of AD 1215. There he had Kamelion take the shape of King John, and he himself assumed the guise of Sir Gilles, a French knight and champion to the King. He planned on stirring up sufficient trouble between the nobility and King John that the Magna Carta would never be signed. His plans were in no manner derailed by the arrival of the Doctor. He simply made allowances, and planned to make the Doctor into the scapegoat for the plot.

However, the Doctor managed to wrest control of Kamelion's mind from the Master and took off in the TARDIS with the shape-shifting robot. He had also managed to sabotage the Master's TARDIS, so that the Master was unable to go where he wished; however, the Master managed to fix the problem and since his scheme to overthrow the Magna Carta was only a minor conceit, he didn't feel that this defeat was really significant.

When the five Doctors were attacked by an unknown foe, the Inner Council on Gallifrey made contact with the Master, offering him both a pardon and a complete new regeneration cycle in exchange for his helping the Doctor. The Master, somewhat reluctantly, agreed to this – the possible prize outweighing the ignominy of helping his worst enemy – although he felt no need of the pardon of his fellow Time Lords. Unfortunately, the Doctor refused to accept the Master's protestations of help, and the Master teamed with the Cybermen within the Death Zone to achieve his own goals. Defeated once again when he tried to gain the ring of Rassilon, the Master was returned by Rassilon to his own TARDIS. Rassilon assured the Doctor that the Master's many sins would one day find him out.

Something of the sort indeed did happen. While experimenting on increasing the power of his Tissue Compression Eliminator, the Master accidentally shrank himself. Unlike other victims of the weapon, the Master was not killed. But he was effectively trapped at six inches in height unless he could restore himself again. He knew of the supply of numismaton gas on the planet Sarn, which has incredible restorative powers. Accordingly, he moved there in his TARDIS, but volcanic activity on the planet resulted in his ship being buried, trapping him aboard.

The Master still retained his mental link with Kamelion, and he forced the unfortunate robot to assume the identity of Professor Howard Foster, guardian of Peri Brown. Coincidentally, Howard had discovered a Trion beacon on the Earth, and Sarn was a Trion penal planet, where Turlough's brother had been sent in exile from his home planet. The Doctor, Turlough and Peri went to Sarn, where Kamelion was completely taken over by the Master. Posing as the promised Outsider, the Master/Kamelion won the trust of Timanov, the high priest, and the Sarn natives freed the Master's TARDIS. The Master managed to make it to the restoring flames of the numismaton gas, but was apparently destroyed when the fires reversed their effects. Despite this setback the Master somehow survived the ordeal, and was restored to his full size once again.

Determined to gain his revenge over the Doctor, the Master set a trap for him in eighteenth-century England. Attempting to harness the creative genius of the minds behind the Industrial Revolution, the Master ran into another renegade, the Rani. He forced her to help him, and the pair of them attempted several times to kill the Doctor, but without any success. The Master's plan of using the Rani's special mind-controlling parasitic worms to harness the great minds of the day failed, and together they fled in her TARDIS. The Doctor had reset the controls, however, and the Master and the Rani were left stranded in the out of control TARDIS, menaced by a growing Tyrannosaurus Rex.

The Master managed to survive. When the Valeyard invaded the Matrix, the Master saw his own chance for a little revenge and profit. Presumably when he had fled Gallifrey in *The Deadly Assassin*, he had

The fifth Doctor and the Master.

The Master in *The Planet of Fire*.

The Master in *Survival*.

taken with him knowledge of how to invade the Matrix, because he managed to tune into it and to discover the Valeyard's plans. He learned that the Sleepers from Andromeda had culled secrets out of the Matrix, and hidden the data on Ravalox. The Master hired Sabalom Glitz to regain this information. Glitz struck out on his own, but the data was lost in the fighting when the Immortal was overthrown.

Undisturbed by the loss, the Master then used his access to the Matrix to stir matters up at the Doctor's mock trial. He tracked down Mel and Glitz and transported them to testify on the Doctor's behalf. This was not done out of kindness to the Doctor, but because the Master was worried about the possible competition in evil that he would face from the Valeyard. Besides this, he enjoyed stirring up trouble for the sanctimonious High Council. He hoped that while the Doctor and the Valeyard fought one another – during which confrontation perhaps one or both might perish – he would be able to gain full control of the Matrix and to take over Gallifrey when the High Council was deposed.

His plans failed because he underestimated both the Valeyard and the Doctor. The Valeyard turned the tables on the Master, defeating his attempts to wrest control of the Matrix out of his hands. The Doctor then used his own ingenuity to cause a temporary breakdown in the Matrix, trapping the Master within until it could be repaired. Though the Master was apparently captured by the Time Lords, he clearly managed somehow to escape them yet again.

Naturally, he returned to solo operations. Somehow he lost his TARDIS in his travels, and was trapped on the planet of the Cheetah people. Through the planet's baleful influence he was beginning to turn into one of them; seeking an escape, he used the Doctor as a sort of mental channel to enable himself to escape back to Earth. Using hypnotized youths to attack the Doctor, the Master managed to escape once again. His current whereabouts are unknown.

CHAPTER 13:

BOROSA

Perhaps more than any other being in the history of the cosmos, Borusa typifies the old adage that power corrupts, and absolute power corrupts absolutely.

Borusa was one of the most high-ranking and well-respected members of the Prydonian Chapter. His background was in jurisprudence, and it was almost natural that he entered politics. He rose to become Cardinal of the Prydonians, the most elevated rank within the Chapter. As such, he was automatically a member of the High Council of the Time Lords.

At the same time, he also taught at the Prydon Academy. Among his pupils there was the Doctor; though contemporaries of the Doctor at the Academy, the Master and the Rani did not attend Borusa's classes as neither had any use for the law. The Doctor's intelligence impressed Borusa, but he did not fully approve of the young Time Lord. 'You will never amount to anything in the galaxy, Doctor,' he informed his former pupil on a number of occasions, 'while you retain your propensity for vulgar facetiousness.'

Despite his love for the law, Borusa saw it merely as a tool to help order society. He was inclined to adjust the truth somewhat, to create what he preferred people to think, rather than to reflect what actually happened – a common failing in the Time Lords. 'If heroes don't exist,' he observed at one point, 'it is necessary to invent them. Good for public morale.' This belief that he ultimately knew what was best for others would eventually lead to his downfall.

He was peripherally involved in the Master's attempts to repower his regenerations on Gallifrey. He observed and commented on the Doctor's fight with the Master, and helped the Doctor in his bid for the Presidency of the Time Lords. When the Doctor left Gallifrey at the end of the affair of *The Deadly*

STORIES:
(1) *The Deadly Assassin*
(2) *The Invasion of Time*
(3) *Arc of Infinity*
(4) *The Five Doctors*

The last regeneration of Lord President Borusa (*The Five Doctors*).

Assassin, the Doctor was elected President by default – the only other candidate, Goth, was dead. Since the Doctor did not serve, then Borusa, as head of the High Council, was appointed Chancellor.

Strictly speaking, this was an illegal move, since only the President can appoint a Chancellor, but in the absence of the Doctor, there was little else to do. The Doctor returned hastily to Gallifrey, however, and claimed his right to become the President (*The Invasion of Time*). Borusa had no option but to comply, although he had initial reservations about the fitness of the Doctor for the post. He quickly realized, however, that the Doctor was playing a very dangerous double game with some alien force, and aided him without appearing to be on his side. As a result, he was actively involved in dispelling both the Vardan and Sontaran attempts to invade and conquer Gallifrey. As soon as the Doctor had succeeded in ridding the Matrix of the invaders, he once again left Gallifrey. This time, however, he placed Borusa firmly in place as President.

Borusa regenerated shortly afterwards, and the changes in his personality began to exert their toll. His new drive was no longer for knowledge but power. He became convinced – correctly – that the Council mostly consisted of ineffectual sheep, and so he engineered the election of officials who were not competent in their positions, allowing him to consolidate power into his own hands. Previously, the post of the President had been mostly ceremonial. Borusa, in his dual role as President and leader of the Council, began to strengthen the powers of the President.

When Omega made his second attack on Gallifrey (*Arc of Infinity*), Borusa was more than willing to slay the Doctor in an attempt to delay Omega. Though he professed to be torn about the issue, he was reluctant in word only – he rushed the execution orders through

Borusa as he appeared in *The Invasion of Time*.

very swiftly. As it happened, the Doctor managed to survive, but this was immaterial to Borusa. He still continued his quest to rule Gallifrey with an iron grip.

He once again regenerated before his next and final encounter with the Doctor. How long he spent ruling the Time Lords can only be guessed at. Certainly, when he encountered the Fifth Doctor, both of them acknowledged that it was a long reign. Considering the fact that Borusa led a very sedentary life, and that at such a leisurely pace each regeneration could last about a thousand years, he was almost certainly in control for several millennia. He became increasingly reluctant to relinquish the reins of power and to allow another person to take over from him. Instead, he bent his mind towards achieving true immortality, and becoming President of the Time Lords for all eternity.

Through his study of the information stored in the Matrix he discovered that the *Black Scrolls of Rassilon*, containing hidden knowledge, still existed. So, too, did the Time Scoop, a device once used in the dark past and long supposed to have been dismantled. Borusa tracked down both, and found that the control room for the Time Scoop was a hidden chamber off the Conference Room for the Inner Council – clearly another of Rassilon's jokes at the expense of others. The room was accessed by a musical key, played on the Harp of Rassilon.

Within the room, Borusa found the controls for the Time Scoop, along with the Coronet of Rassilon – a device that accentuated the will of the wearer, bringing other people under his mental control. Using the Time Scoop, Borusa reactivated the Death Zone and began to populate it. Once the setting for gladiatorial combats in the pre-Rassilon era, the Death Zone surrounded the Dark Tower, the Tomb Of Rassilon. Within the Tomb was a force field generator that prevented direct access to it. It was essential that the

Borusa with Chancellery Guards (*Arc of Infinity*).

force field be closed down, and to Borusa's now warped mind, the obvious person to do this was the Doctor.

It was obvious that the Doctor would never work willingly for Borusa in this quest, so the President began draining power from the Eye of Harmony, and he snatched four of the five incarnations of the Doctor then existing out of time and placed them within the Death Zone. To hide his true aims, he also transported several of the Doctor's companions there, and a number of his old foes. Knowing that it would be apparent that whoever was performing all of these illegal actions had to be a high-ranking Time Lord, Borusa then subverted one of the Chancellery Guard captains, and framed the Castellan for the deeds.

It was a sign of how far from his own lofty ideals Borusa had fallen that he would even consider the framing and murder of an honourable and efficient Time Lord. Without a qualm, he had the Castellan executed in order to cover his own tracks and to give him more time. Finally, however, the Doctors managed to breach the Dark Tower and switch off the force field. Borusa then entered the Tomb to claim his prize of immortality from Rassilon himself.

What Borusa's corrupted mind had overlooked was the truth – this was no more than a trap laid down countless ages before by Rassilon. It was Rassilon's plan to ferret out and remove forever all would-be despots, and Borusa had followed a carefully-laid trail right into a trap. When he claimed the gift of immortality, Rassilon granted to him the immortality of becoming living stone. Borusa now had his prize, the curse of immortality – his mind trapped forever within an immobile body.

The third, second and first Doctors (*The Five Doctors*).

CHAPTER 14:

THE RANI

T he female Time Lord known as the Rani (a Hindu word that means a reigning queen) is an imperious, amoral character, without qualms or conscience. She considers all other species as vastly lesser forms of life, to be exploited or butchered as her needs may be. Her only passion in life is in her experiments, which are frequently highly dangerous and often lethal to other beings.

She, the Doctor and the Master are all of the same age, 953 as last given, and attended the University together. While the Doctor specialized in thermodynamics, the Rani concentrated on biochemistry. A genius in this field, she is less well versed with physics, but has a tremendous grasp of time theory.

After an experiment went awry – she turned the President's mice into horrendous monsters that devoured his pet cat – she was unwisely exiled from Gallifrey by the Time Lords. They had hoped that forced absence from her scientific apparatus – she had neither family nor friends – would make her more malleable. As usual, the Time Lords erred. Instead of wanting to return to her home world, the Rani took her place on the planet of Miasimia Goria.

She enslaved the native race, placing them under her absolute control. However, she wanted their work rate to be increased, and she fed them an experimental drug that went wrong. It deprived the natives of the ability to rest, and their overtaxed minds then twisted, sending them on rampages of uncontrollable fury. The only way that she could temper these attacks was to steal from the brains of human beings the chemical that enables them to sleep, and then feed this to the Miasimians.

She set up her base of operations on the Earth, in various stages of its more violent history: the Trojan Wars, the Dark Ages, the American War of Independ-

STORIES:
Mark of the Rani
Time and the Rani

The Rani (*Time and the Rani*).

The Rani as she first appeared in *The Mark of the Rani*.

ence and finally the Industrial Revolution in England. Using her machinery and her skill with disguises, she managed to extract the pitifully small quantities of the chemical from the minds of her victims, and then fed it to the Miasimians. On her final visit to the Earth, however, things did not go so well for her.

By coincidence, the Master had selected the same time and place as the setting for one of his elaborate traps for the Doctor. On learning that the Rani was present, the Master managed to hold hostage her vial of the brain extract, and forced her to aid him in his scheme for revenge. Though the Rani had neither a desire nor taste for revenge, she had no choice but to aid him. From her point of view it became vital that she do so once the Doctor discovered that she was operating on the humans, since he felt compelled to stop her.

The Rani had grown several dozen special parasitic worms that sapped the will, leaving victims of her pets susceptible to her mind control. Using her hypnotized minions and the sleep-deprived humans, she and the Master attempted several times to kill the Doctor, without success. He, meanwhile, had discovered the Rani's plans and he worked against her to combat them. He sabotaged the Rani's TARDIS, setting a trap for her and the Master. Narrowly evading horrific 'land mines' that the Rani had planted, which turned animal life into trees, the Doctor forced both the Rani and the Master to escape in her TARDIS.

The Doctor had set the controls to overload, and the forces in the timeship hurled the pair against the walls, and pinned them there, unable to reach the controls until they burned out. Meanwhile, a foetus of a Tyrannosaurus Rex that she was growing was accelerated by time spillage into a ravenous adult which menaced her and the Master. Somehow, though, both survived the attack. The Rani jettisoned the Master as soon as she could, and returned to her own plans.

Abandoning Miasimia Goria (either from lack of interest or other, unexplained, reasons), the Rani attempted her grandest experiment: manipulation of time on a huge scale. She had discovered what was apparently an asteroid, composed entirely of 'Strange Matter'. This odd material was the core of an exploded star, matter compressed in on itself by gravitational collapse. The densest known material,

The Rani disguised as a washer-woman (*The Mark of the Rani*).

it produces strange gravitational effects, and the Rani knew that if it could be triggered into exploding, the resultant energy release could be harnessed and used to produce a vast amount of chronons – the component particles of time.

The asteroid was in the same system as the planet Lakertya. The Rani knew the inhabitants of this world as a lazy, pleasure-loving race who would give her no trouble. To be certain, she laid her plans well, enlisting the brutal aid of the bat-like Tetraps in controlling the Lakertyans. She also took two hostages – the Lakertyan ruler, Beyus, and his daughter, Sarn. Both were much more technologically minded and compliant than the rather brutal Tetraps. Finally, she installed within the Lakertyan Centre of Leisure a globe containing millions of insects, whose sting would be deadly to the native race. In the event that the Lakertyans would not obey her bidding, she would release the insects and destroy the entire intelligent race.

Then she set about kidnapping the greatest geniuses of all time, harnessing them together and pooling their mental abilities to create an artificial mind.

The only known way of controlling Strange Matter was to use other Strange Matter – which she did not possess. She needed the pooled mind to tell her how to control the strange matter without her own supply, and to calculate the exact trajectory of the rocket that would ignite the Strange Matter and initiate her scheme.

The key to the plan was to form helium 2, which would strike the atmosphere of Lakertya and produce a flood of chronons. The resulting reaction would, naturally, kill every living being left on the planet, but that was of little concern to her. The problem was that she simply couldn't design the controlling mechanism properly, nor did her collected minds have sufficient intelligence to finish the calculations. What she needed, unfortunately, was the Doctor.

She had mastered remote control units for TARDISes, and using one of these, she dragged the Doctor's TARDIS violently out of the space-time vortex. In the resultant crash, the Doctor was injured, and regenerated. Seizing her chance, the Rani took advantage of his post-regeneration shock and induced partial amnesia into him. She fooled him into believing that she was actually his companion, Mel, and managed to get him to repair her broken machinery. Then she hooked him into the mind-set.

What she had not anticipated was that his personality would disrupt the bonding of the minds into one great thinking apparatus. He induced psychic schizophrenia instead, and she was forced to isolate him. However, the Doctor had enabled the brain to complete its task, and the Rani set her plan into motion, then headed for her TARDIS to escape the impending destruction of Lakertya. The Doctor and the natives managed to sabotage the controls, however, and the rocket launched too late to explode the asteroid. If this were not bad enough, the Rani's escape was dashed when she entered her TARDIS. Her Tetraps had discovered that she had intended to allow them to perish, and instead they hijacked her TARDIS. The Rani was taken captive by the Tetraps, who intended to use her genius to help their own people.

Since her capture, nothing has been heard from the Rani. It would be premature to say that she may not yet escape the Tetraps and return to her insane experiments.

The Rani with the giant brain she created in *Time and the Rani*.

CHAPTER 15:

THE VALEYARD

On the occasion of his second trial by the Time Lords, the Doctor was snatched out of time and dragged to an orbital station, presumably above Gallifrey. Here, he was faced by a court composed of observers from the Ultimate Court of Appeal under the guidance of the Inquisitor. The prosecution took the shape of a strange figure known as the Valeyard.

The Doctor was accused of 'conduct unbecoming a Time Lord' and with transgressing the First Law, that of non-interference – an interesting point, since the First Law of Time has been clearly stated in the past as being a law against a Time Lord meeting future or past incarnations of himself or herself. Presumably since the High Council had in fact transgressed that law themselves, they had replaced it with the law on non-interference. The Valeyard demanded the death penalty for the Doctor, and his forfeiture of all future regenerations.

The Valeyard presented two examples of what he claimed were the Doctor's actions, though both were subtly distorted. The first concerned the affairs of the planet Ravalox. According to the Matrix records, Ravalox had been devastated by a fireball and left lifeless. The Doctor investigated this claim, and found it far from true. In fact, the surface was bursting with vegetation, and a colony of survivors had lived through the fireball in UK Habitat. This was ruled by the Immortal, an L3 robot named Drathro. Drathro had attempted to run an efficient survival colony involving culling of excess population, even though the planet surface was now viable again. Instead of performing the cullings, Merdeen, one of his guards, had been allowing the 'victims' to escape to the surface, where they became the Tribe of the Free, under the rule of Queen Katryca.

Complicating matters, a mercenary of all trades, Sabalom Glitz and his dim-witted assistant, Dibber,

STORIES:
*The Trial of a Time Lord
[The Mysterious Planet,
Mindwarp,
Terror of the Vervoids
and The Ultimate Foe]*

The Valeyard (*The Trial of a Time Lord*).

The Inquisitor and the sixth Doctor (*The Trial of a Timelord*).

arrived. They had been informed by the Master that the Sleepers – who had constructed Drathro – had stolen secrets of great value. The Valeyard had the identity of these secrets stricken from the record, as well as the fact that Ravalox was actually the planet Earth. Subtly twisting the facts to suit his case, he used the Doctor's interference in the events on Ravalox as a claim that the Doctor endangered the lives of lesser beings with his interference.

The Valeyard's second example was the Doctor's trip to Thoros Beta. This was the home world of the Mentors, one of whom, Sil, the Doctor had met before. The Mentors were trading advanced weapons to Thoros Alpha, a warrior-populated world. The Doctor wanted this stopped in order to prevent contamination of the culture. He discovered that King Yrcanos, one of the war chiefs of Alpha, had been kidnapped by the Mentors and was being 'influenced' to buy from them. Yrcanos and the Doctor's current companion, Peri, were forced to fight for their lives, with the Doctor apparently turned traitor against them.

In fact, he had been affected by the mind probe used on him by the Mentors' tame scientist, Crozier. It had made the Doctor unstable and selfish, and the Valeyard used this as evidence against him. Because of the effects of the probe, the Doctor couldn't remember what had actually happened, and was therefore unable to defend any of his actions. Crozier's main experiment was in transferring the brain (and, later, simply the memories and personality) of one being into another. The Time Lords could not allow this to succeed, as they believed that it would violate the natural state of the Universe. They apparently didn't care when one of their own did this same feat, since the Master had assumed the body of Tremas of Traken in this manner without punishment. The Master had, of course, also grossly interfered with the development of many worlds, and had never been sentenced to termination – punishment that faced the Doctor in this court on lesser charges. Clearly, then, Time Lord justice is as inexplicable as human justice.

When Crozier attempted to transfer the mind of

The sixth Doctor refuting the Valeyard's accusations (*The Trial of a Time Lord*).

the Mentor Kiv into the body of Peri, the Doctor was snatched out of time to answer to the Tribunal. Peri was apparently killed, her body possessed by Kiv. Yrcanos, a puppet of the Time Lords, then assassinated both Peri/Kiv and Crozier. We were later told that this was not what had happened, but a brilliant distortion of the truth by the Valeyard to unsettle the Doctor. As the Master revealed later, what actually transpired was that Yrcanos had arrived in time to save Peri, and simply killed Kiv and Crozier. Yrcanos then took Peri back to Thoros Alpha as his queen.

In his own defence, the Doctor called forth the events still to come in his life – assuming that he was allowed one. He and his companion Mel would be on the star liner *Hyperion III* in AD 2986. There, Professor Lasky and her assistants Doland and Bruckner would be transporting the Vervoids – intelligent plants that they had created, and a terrible menace to all other living creatures. Also aboard the ship would be Mogarians, creatures who objected to the Earth's exploitation of their home world. Someone would be killing off members of the crew, and the Doctor and Mel would make a frenetic attempt to uncover the culprit. In the end, however, all would be futile once the Vervoids awakened. They would bear a terrible

hatred for 'animalkind', which preys on plant-life. If they ever reached the Earth, the Vervoids would kill not merely all humans but all animal life there.

Faced with this, the Doctor simply would have no choice but the utter eradication of the Vervoids. Using incredibly intense light, the Doctor would accelerate the Vervoids through their life-cycles in seconds, until they perished totally. Even a single living leaf could regenerate into a Vervoid and doom the other life-forms of the Universe. The Valeyard, however, had subtly altered the records, and now used this defence of the Doctor's as a claim that he had committed genocide by killing an entire intelligent species – the Vervoids. Under Article 7 of the Gallifreyan Constitution, the Valeyard now claimed that the Doctor should be judicially killed.

The Doctor appeared to be trapped, since without further time he could not prove that the records in the Matrix had been falsified. However, the Master came to his aid, sending both Sabalom Glitz and Mel to refute the testimony of the Valeyard, and to expose the Valeyard for who he truly was – the Doctor.

The Master had managed to learn the truth and

The sixth Doctor with Mr Popplewick, the disguise adopted by the Valeyard in the Matrix (*The Trial of a Time Lord*).

now revealed it to the assembled court. The High Council was attempting to cover its own corruption and was using the Valeyard to do this. Ravalox was in fact the planet Earth, whose population had been almost completely killed when the High Council had had the world shifted to its current position and renamed Ravalox. Knowing that the Doctor would discover this – Earth being, after all, the Doctor's home away from home – the High Council trumped up charges against the Doctor in order to have him legally assassinated. The Valeyard was the tool by which they hoped to accomplish the murder.

The Valeyard was the distillation of the evil side of the Doctor, a shadowy figure that might exist somewhere beyond the Doctor's twelfth and final regenerations. The High Council had promised the Valeyard all of the Doctor's remaining regenerations if he succeeded in his twin tasks. First, the Doctor had to perish, ostensibly as a result of a 'fair trial'. Secondly, to avoid the trial being shown up as a sham, the Ultimate Court of Appeal had also to die. The Valeyard planned on doing this through the Matrix, where he had established a particle disseminator, a Maser that would kill all viewing that section of the Matrix.

The Doctor invaded the Matrix and with the somewhat erratic aid of Glitz and Mel, he succeeded in stopping the attempted murder of the Court of Appeal. He temporarily fused the Matrix, apparently trapping both the Master and the Valeyard. The Doctor was then cleared of all charges, and the populace of Gallifrey rose up against the corrupt High Council, deposing it and instigating elections for fresh officials. The Valeyard, however, was not trapped, and instead managed to take over the body of the Keeper of the Matrix.

Speculation

How had all of this come about?

The Time Lords had already wrecked the Doctor's own past by their continual interference in all of his previous incarnations (see Chapter 6). The corrupt High Council presumably seized upon this, and began to manipulate his future lives. At his initial trial before the Time Lords, the Doctor was offered a number of different possible future incarnations, all of which he rejected (The War Games). When the first Romana had to regenerate, we saw that she had her own options as to the final form that her own next regeneration could take (Destiny of the Daleks). And when the Time Lord K'Anpo had to regenerate, his next incarnation, Cho-je, carried on a separate existence for a while beforehand (Planet of the Spiders). Even the Doctor had met one of his future selves in the form of the Watcher (Logopolis). It is quite clear, then, that the business of regeneration is not a simple set pattern of inevitability. There is always room for flux and change.

The High Council must therefore have carefully selected future incarnations for the Doctor from among the many possibilities open to him. They would then have manipulated those choices so that the Doctor's last incarnation would be the embodiment of all that was evil within the Doctor – the Valeyard. Then, using their temporal abilities, this potential Doctor could be brought into current Gallifrey. That the Doctor might

have a dark side had been shown when he regenerated to the Sixth Doctor. In a fit of near-insanity, he had attacked and almost killed Peri. Whatever the Doctor might wish to think about himself, he clearly has the potential inside himself to be evil. And nothing could be more evil than a good person totally corrupted.

The Valeyard thus would not exist if the Doctor were to continue unaffected by the manipulations of the Time Lords. With the High Council now deposed, the Valeyard will never come to be as part of the Doctor that we know. However, the High Council had managed to create a living being from his potential. The Valeyard could be stabilized only through the destruction of the Doctor – or so they believed.

However, it seems more than likely that the Valeyard had his own plans. He would never remain in the shadow of the High Council, covering for them, and had already laid his own schemes to gain his life independently of them. He had complete access to the Matrix, and the information that it contained, including the knowledge of Crozier's mental transference process. Using this method, the Valeyard most likely transferred his own mind from his trapped body and projected it into the one being who was still in contact with the Matrix – its Keeper. The Keeper's own mind and persona would have been destroyed, but the Valeyard lives on, within his body.

Turlough, the alien exile who was the unwilling agent of the Black Guardian (*Mawdryn Undead*).

CHAPTER 16

THE GUARDIANS

The Guardians are mysterious beings, existing outside the normal Universes of space and time. There are two Guardians, White and Black, equal in power and who are almost exactly complementary in temperaments and intentions. Just how great their powers may be remains unknown.

They exist to maintain the balance between good and evil in the Universe. However, while the Black Guardian strives to destroy his counterpart and to plunge the Universes into chaos and despair, the White Guardian seeks only to maintain the balance between good and evil.

They cannot act directly in events in this continuum, but they can empower other beings to act for them. When one chooses a champion for a given purpose, the other somehow knows and can oppose his actions with a champion of his own. They are forced to accept the results of the ensuing battle. Over the millennia, the balance of power has swung between the two of them a number of times.

The Time Lords know of their existence, but can hardly ever interact with them. Normal beings cannot contact a Guardian. However, Guardians can intrude physically into the space-time continuum in order to recruit their agents. They have the ability to stop even a TARDIS while it is in the Vortex and to drain its power, should they so choose – providing they know where to find the craft. But they are neither omnipotent nor omniscient. The Doctor was able to hide from the Black Guardian for a considerable period of time using a randomizer device fitted to his TARDIS.

The Guardians do not need to be physically located, as normal beings must. Nor do they need to breathe, eat or sleep. They have the ability to create temporary habitats about themselves for the convenience of the

THE BLACK GUARDIAN
STORIES:
The Armageddon Factor
Mawdryn Undead
Terminus
Enlightenment

The Black Guardian (*Mawdryn Undead*).

The White Guardian (*The Ribos Operation*).

**THE WHITE GUARDIAN
STORIES:**
*The Ribos Operation
Enlightenment*

mortals that they communicate with, but have no need of such an environment for themselves.

The Doctor was first contacted by the White Guardian when there was a time of impending chaos. He was asked to search for the six scattered segments of the Key to Time. Once reassembled into a perfect cube, the Key could stop the motion of all particles within the Universe for a brief span of time, in order to maintain the balance of the Universe. The Black Guardian also sought the Key in order to use it to ensure the prevalence of eternal chaos.

The six keys had been disguised and scattered through time and space to make them deliberately difficult to locate. The Doctor was given a locating device which also served as the Core to the Key, holding it together when the pieces were found and joined. With the assistance of his companion Romana, assigned to him by the White Guardian, the Doctor recovered the six segments of the Key, and finally assembled it.

The Black Guardian had not been idle, however. He, too, had enlisted the aid of an agent, a strange being known only as the Shadow. A dark, warped creature, the Shadow was apparently an immortal being who loved chaos and fear and could dominate the minds of others. (It is possible that he, too, was a Time Lord, but his origin was never clarified.) He waited for the Doctor to complete his collection of the first five segments as he had already identified and obtained the final segment – the Princess Astra of Atrios. The Doctor managed to defeat the Shadow, who was killed when his Planet of Fear was destroyed by the Marshal of Atrios.

The Black Guardian then posed as the White Guardian in an attempt to trick the Doctor into releasing the Key to him. However, because of the callous way in which the Guardian dismissed the fate of Astra, the Doctor saw through the trick and instead of handing over the Key, the Doctor dispersed it once again into the unknown limits of time and space, in the process restoring Astra to her human form. Thwarted in his plans, the Black Guardian swore to get his revenge on the Doctor.

Since the Doctor had dispersed the Key before the White Guardian had used it to stabilize the Universe,

The fourth Doctor with the Marshall of Atrios, who helped him defeat the Shadow, an agent of the Black Guardian ·

does this mean that he had failed in his quest, and that the Universe is now on its way into a state of utter chaos? Perhaps not. The Guardian had explained that it was necessary to stop every particle in the Universe for a brief span of time in order to relieve the stresses on the continuum. The Doctor had in fact done this himself when he assembled the Key and used it to prevent the Marshal from destroying Zeos. For a short moment, the Key suspended all motion in the Universe, and this may well have been sufficient for the stresses to have been relieved. If this were not the case, then why did only the Black Guardian appear to collect the Key? He must have known that the White Guardian's task was finished, and that he would be unobstructed in his plan to trick the Doctor by posing as the White Guardian.

With the failure of his plan, the Black Guardian began to plot the destruction of the Doctor. He was thwarted for a while by the Doctor's use of the Randomizer, but the Doctor eventually removed the device from his TARDIS (*The Leisure Hive*), and the Black Guardian was finally able to trace him.

Unable to interfere directly with the Doctor, the Black Guardian instead sought an agent to work through. Knowing of the Doctor's impending arrival at a British public school, The Black Guardian found his agent there in the form of Turlough. Turlough was an alien being, human in appearance, who had been stranded on the Earth and who desired more than anything to escape. The Guardian offered him his freedom on the condition that he kill the Doctor. Turlough – who could be quite ruthless when he put his mind to it – agreed to the terms.

To the Black Guardian's frustration, however, Turlough proved to be a poor choice. His pathetic attempts to destroy the Doctor invariably failed, and it soon became quite clear that Turlough had grown to like and even admire the Doctor, and that he would never destroy the wandering Time Lord. Accordingly, the Black Guardian decided to abandon Turlough at a point where he had another agent who might succeed in killing the Doctor.

Both Black and White Guardians knew of the

existence of the Eternals (*Enlightenment*), a race of beings that exist outside of Time itself. Immortal, unchanging and endlessly seeking diversion, the Eternals robbed the minds of Ephemerals – those beings implanted in Time – for their own amusement. The Guardians had sponsored a race through space in solar-powered sailing ships, and the prize that would be offered to the winner would be Enlightenment.

To the Eternals, this was the ultimate prize – the wisdom to be able to achieve what they most desired. A number of them entered into the race, including Striker and his First Officer, Marriner. Both sought to win, but fairly. Not all were so scrupulous – especially since cheating wasn't actually against the rules and was simply considered poor form. Worst were Wrack, and her First Officer Mansell, who appropriately manifested themselves as pirates in the race.

Wrack was also secretly the agent of the Black Guardian. In his usual lying way, he had promised her power over her foes in return for her service, and she had accepted. Focusing her own powers with the extra abilities bestowed upon her by the Black Guardian, she then destroyed her opponents, one by one. The White Guardian saw the plan of his evil counterpart – to allow Wrack to win the prize. In her case, she would use Enlightenment to rape the inhabitants of Time and plunge the Universe into eternal chaos. The White Guardian attempted to contact the Doctor to seek his aid in stopping Wrack, but his powers were sapped by the Black Guardian, and he could only manage a cryptic warning.

Nonetheless, the Doctor did succeed in figuring out what was happening. With the aid of Turlough – who had finally taken a stand as to whose side he was on – the Doctor defeated Wrack and Mansell, and he and Turlough were at the helm of the first ship to complete the course. They were accordingly awarded the prize. The Doctor turned it down, but the Black Guardian sought one last time to have Turlough kill the Doctor. Turlough spurned this offer, causing the Black Guardian to temporarily dissolve. Enlightenment, it turned out, was the act of choosing, and Turlough had found what he most needed – peace.

The Black Guardian was not destroyed, however. 'While I exist, he exists also,' the White Guardian explained, 'until we are no longer needed.' They are the equal and opposite halves of one great power. They are the embodiments of light and dark, good and evil, right and wrong. Their purpose is to guide and protect, as their name implies, those weaker and less advanced than they themselves are. It may be that they will continue in this function for the rest of eternity.

Captain Wrack, an agent of the Black Guardian, with the fifth Doctor (*Enlightenment*).

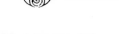

CHAPTER 17:

THE RENEGADES

In this chapter, the term 'renegade' is applied only to those Time Lords who have left their home world of Gallifrey. It does not necessarily suggest that the being is evil.

THE WAR CHIEF

STORY:
The War Games

The War Chief was a Time Lord who decided to leave the stagnant society of Gallifrey and to branch out on his own. He stole several SIDRAT machines – devices akin to the TARDIS, but capable of being remotely controlled, and without the chameleon circuits to disguise their appearance – and joined forces with the War Lord and his alien horde. Together they devised a plan to kidnap soldiers from the various wars of Earth and to then mould them into the greatest fighting force ever assembled. Using this force, they would then conquer the Galaxy. 'Man is the most vicious species of all,' he informed the Doctor, explaining their choice of pawns.

The War Chief aimed to double-cross the War Lord and his alien allies and then take over the reins of power himself; though he claimed to be working for the cause of peace, he had developed a taste for power. His plans were destroyed by the arrival of the Doctor. Despite his having changed his appearance since he had left their home world, the War Chief recognized him. The Doctor, however, did not know the War Chief personally, so presumably the War Chief had never directly crossed the Doctor's path back on Gallifrey. Though he attempted to enlist the Doctor's help, the War Chief's plans began to crumble about him. In fury, he killed the Security Chief of the aliens, a being he had constantly feuded with. The War Chief in his turn was then slain by the surviving troops of the War Lord.

CHO-JE/K'ANPO

STORY:
Planet of the Spiders

In *The Time Monster*, the Doctor tells Jo Grant about an ancient hermit who lived in a cave at the top of a mountain, and who taught him a valuable lesson about life. In *State of Decay*, the Doctor mentions that the mountains were in South Gallifrey, and that the hermit also told him a number of ghost stories.

The hermit only appeared once in person, and that was in *Planet of the Spiders*. There we find out that he

The third Doctor and K'Anpo (*Planet of the Spiders*).

taught the Doctor to understand his own mind, and to face his feelings and beliefs. He apparently had something to do with the Doctor's decision to 'borrow' a TARDIS and leave Gallifrey. He, too, disliked what the Time Lords had become. 'The discipline they serve is not for me,' he observed. Instead, he left Gallifrey – apparently through some form of mental projection, since he does not have a TARDIS and has the power of teleporting himself without one. He arrived on the Earth, where he assumed the identity of Abbot K'Anpo Rimpoche in Tibet.

He then moved to England, setting up a meditation centre where he knew he would be most needed. He foresaw the Doctor's battle with the giant spiders of Metabelis Three, and was ready to aid as best he could. He also projected forward in time his next regeneration, that of Cho-je. As such, he was undoubtedly breaking the First Law of Time, but he needed the mobility of his new body. He helped the Doctor to understand that the only way to fight the spiders was to face them down, and that his own fears were the real enemy here. The Doctor defeated the spiders, but his body was physically ravaged in every cell. K'Anpo/Cho-je then helped him to regenerate into his fourth body.

MORBIUS
AND THE SISTERHOOD OF KARN

STORY:
The Brain of Morbius

Morbius once led the High Council of the Time Lords, though precisely when this was is not made clear. A greedy, bitter man, he despised his fellow Time Lords as 'pallid, devious worms', and he did not agree with their policy of non-interference. He believed that they had been given their great powers in order to rule all lesser species. He tried to convince the High Council to go along with him in this ambition, but they completely rejected him.

Furious but undaunted, he left Gallifrey and raised an army of millions of followers, the scum of the Universe, aiming to conquer every world with their aid. To establish their loyalty, he told them of the Sisterhood of Karn and their Elixir of Life. In that time, Karn was a green and prosperous planet, and the Sisterhood an elite cadre of the population. Led by

Maren, they served the Flame of Life within their mountain shrine. The Flame was actually an ignited upventing of natural gas from within Karn's interior. It burnt within a cavity, and its heat worked on the moisture that seeped through the rocks, producing the Elixir. Anyone drinking from this Elixir would be healed of their wounds and have their life preserved as it then was. However, constant drinks of the Elixir were needed to sustain this immortality.

Until Morbius revealed the secret, it was known only to the Sisterhood and to the Time Lords. The Sisters would provide small amounts of the Elixir to the Time Lords, who used it for its regenerative qualities to help in difficult regenerations. Once Morbius told his followers, though, Karn was their goal, as they aimed to seize the supply for themselves. They left several barren planets in their wake until they gathered on Karn and destroyed its surface almost entirely.

The Time Lords had been expecting this move, however, and they chose Karn for their own counter-

The Brain of Morbius in its constructed body (*The Brain of Morbius*).

Solon attacked by his creation (*The Brain of Morbius*).

The fourth Doctor and Sarah Jane with the Sisterhood of Karn (*The Brain of Morbius*).

attack. Morbius's rag-tag army was annihilated, and the renegade was captured. He was tried publicly on Karn for his crimes, and then placed in a dispersal chamber. His atoms were then scattered to 'the nine corners of the Universe', as Ohica later told the tale.

Certain that Morbius's threat was over, the Time Lords then let their attention wander from Karn. Even the Sisterhood, despite their vast mental powers, did not know that Morbius still lived. He had enlisted the aid of one of his more fanatical followers, Mehendri Solon, a neurosurgeon of almost insane genius. Though Morbius's body had perished, Solon had removed his brain, and kept it alive in a colloidal suspension. Morbius viewed this as living death, enduring it for as long as he had to while Solon perfected his techniques to enable him to graft the brain back into a specially constructed body.

In order to keep their Elixir safe, the Sisterhood had managed to establish a telekinetic force field about Karn which would destroy the craft of any beings foolish enough to venture too close to the planet. They also practised the sacrifice of offenders from time to time. Solon used the crashed spaceships as fodder to construct a new body for Morbius. All that he was missing was a head with a cranial capacity large enough to take the brain. Meanwhile, the Sisters were having problems with the Flame and their supply of Elixir. For the first time, the Flame seemed to be dying.

Whether it was this lack of Elixir or because of their worries about Solon's activities, the Time Lords directed the TARDIS to Karn. Initially furious ('there's something going on here, some dirty work they won't touch with their lily-white hands!'), the Doctor investigated the problem. He helped the Sisters to restore the Flame by clearing the soot from the passage that fed the gases to the ignition chamber. Solon attempted to use the Doctor as a source for the head he needed, but constantly failed to get it. When Morbius was told that the Doctor was a Time Lord, he panicked. Thinking that they had finally tracked him down and were about to kill him again, Morbius insisted that Solon transfer his brain into an artificial 'head' of plastic and electronics. Solon reluctantly complied, but was afraid that the static electricity that would result might ground through the brain, driving Morbius insane.

Solon had a more real problem, though, when Condo – his brutish assistant – allowed the brain to fall on the floor during the operation, damaging it. When connected into the artificial skull, Morbius awoke with only the baser reflexes operating. Lurching in his mis-matched body from the laboratory, he killed one of the Sisters before he could be subdued. Solon finished the operation, allowing Morbius to possess some form of rational thought. The Doctor managed to slay Solon, but Morbius was now alive and moving again. He was all set to begin raising another army for conquest, but the Doctor challenged him to a mind-bending contest.

Mend-bending was supposed to be a Time Lord game, in which two opponents pitted their intelligences against each other. The loser was supposed to be able to pull out of the competition, but if the winner pressed home the advantage, then the loser could be killed. Morbius aimed for this to happen to the Doctor, and tried to regress the Doctor mentally through his previous incarnations. Until his brain overheated he was unaware that the Doctor was actually winning the battle. Unable to think rationally, Morbius staggered away, and was driven to his death by the now-mobilized Sisters.

DRAX

STORY:
The Armageddon Factor

Drax was in the Academy at the same time as the Doctor, the class of '92. However, Drax wasn't very academically accomplished and failed his Temporal Theory. He did, however, excel with his hands, and he moved into repair and maintenance. Proving to be more than capable in those fields, he stole a TARDIS and set off on his own to make a few business transactions across the Universe. With his skill, he was in great demand for fieldwork in cybernetics, guidance systems and armaments – though he wasn't too fond of the latter.

He had something of the crook and something of the con artist in him, and from time to time tried to appropriate things that by no stretch of the imagination could be considered as his or as legitimate salvage. One attempt at such a theft (in order to repair his TARDIS) left him in the hands of the law in London, Earth. As a result, he spent ten years in Brixton Prison. While he was there, he picked up a thick accent and vocabulary suiting the area, which

The fourth Doctor and Drax (*The Armageddon Factor*).

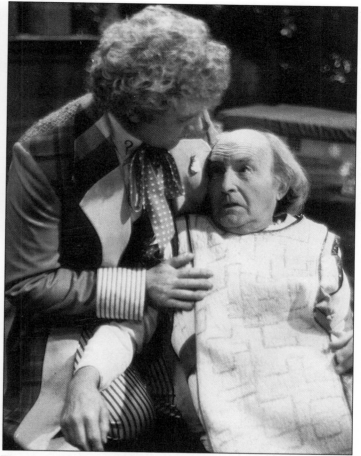

The sixth Doctor and Azmael (*The Twin Dilemma*).

he retained in later years when he returned to time and space travel.

He was contacted by the Shadow for a simple job of building a computer. Unaware of the identity of his latest business contact, Drax became accidentally separated from his TARDIS, and found himself forced under threat of death to assist the plans of the Shadow. Drax had little option but to go along and do as he was told. He constructed Mentalis, a sophisticated computer that the Shadow used to wage a devastating war between the twin planets of Zeos and Atrios. For the five long years of the war, until he once again made contact with the Doctor, Drax was a prisoner of the Shadow. Working together, both of them managed to end the war and to prevent the Shadow from getting his hands on the Key to Time. With the war over, Drax elected to stay behind and do a bit of salvage work on the war-torn Atrios, taking the now out-of-work Marshal of Atrios on as an almost-equal partner.

AZMAEL

STORY:
The Twin Dilemma

Azmael was an old Time Lord who had once been one of the Doctor's teachers at the Academy. The Doctor, perhaps in flattery, claimed that Azmael was the best of them all. At any rate, he grew dissatisfied with life on Gallifrey, and left there to settle on the planet Jaconda. There he became the Master of Jaconda, the kindly ruler of the bird-derived native species. In an unshown tale, the Doctor met him there again while in his own fourth incarnation, and the two managed to crack more than a few bottles of spirits in a memorable evening.

Later, though, giant gastropods invaded the world. The leader of these, Mestor, possessed great mental powers, and even greater ambitions. He planned to explode Jaconda's sun and thus spread his own eggs to the corners of the Universe, where his descendants would rule. Using his mental powers, Mestor forced Azmael to cooperate in his insane plans.

Under the name of Professor Edgeworth, Azmael kidnapped Romulus and Remus, two teenage twins of advanced mathematical genius, from the Earth. The Doctor, freshly regenerated into his sixth body, ran across them all and became involved with helping his old friend. Once the Doctor had deduced the entire plan, he and Azmael confronted Mestor. Azmael, having used up all of his regenerations, triggered a final one while possessed by Mestor's mind. This killed both the giant slug and Azmael.

One of the Time Lords who allowed the third Doctor to leave Earth to thwart the Master (*The Colony in Space*).

CHAPTER 18:

OTHER TIME LORDS

There have been over the years a number of Time Lords who have appeared to either help or hinder the Doctor. Many of these were Gallifrey-based, and hence do not qualify as renegades.

The War Games

The Tribunal of Time Lords appeared in this story only, though they are referred to in *Terror of the Autons*. The three members judged and condemned the War Lord and his race for their actions in creating and operating the War Games. They then tried the Doctor for his crimes of interference, and condemned him to exile on Earth.

Zoe, Jamie and the second Doctor alongside members of the tribunal of Time Lords (*The War Games*).

Terror of the Autons

The somewhat sarcastic Time Lord in this story was sent by the Tribunal to warn the Doctor of the Master's escape from Gallifrey. The Doctor and he had clearly met before, as he mocked the Doctor's style of dress over the years, and the Doctor disparaged his attempts at wit.

Colony in Space

The Time Lords in this story were in charge of security, and discovered that the Master had managed to steal the information about the Doomsday Weapon (presumably before his departure from Gallifrey in *Terror of the Autons*). They were presumably members of the Celestial Intervention Agency, and were able to override the Tribunal's decision to exile the Doctor. They restarted his TARDIS for one flight, to enable him to stop the Master from taking control of the Doomsday Weapon. They are presumably the Time Lords who sent the Doctor on his next two missions, in *The Curse of Peladon* and *The Mutants*.

The Three Doctors

When Omega attacked his home world of Gallifrey, we were shown the operations within the Time Control Room. The Time Lords shown were the technicians operating the devices there. In charge of them was the President, though at this point he was technically answerable to the Chancellor. The Chancellor seemed more worried about following form and protocol than the President, who made decisions with practised and informed ease.

Genesis Of The Daleks

The Time Lord in this story took the Doctor and his companions to early Skaro. The Time Lords had foreseen a time when the Daleks 'will have destroyed every other life form and become the dominant creature in the Universe' – presumably through use of the predictive powers of the Matrix. They wanted the Doctor either to avert the creation of the Daleks, or alter their original genetic material to make them less aggressive, or else to find some inherent weakness in them at the point of their creation.

The President wearing the Sash of Rasillon.

The Deadly Assassin

THE PRESIDENT

The first stage in the Master's gambit to destroy Gallifrey and regain his regenerative ability was the murder of the retiring President of the Time Lords. The unnamed President was about to nominate his successor, as was his right, as well as naming several awards to various Time Lords, as was the custom. The President intended to make a few controversial decisions, but was slain before he could do so.

CHANCELLOR GOTH

Goth was an ambitious man, with a gnawing hunger for power in his soul. It was this hunger that the Master exploited in making Goth his dupe. Goth had already become the Chancellor of the Prydonians, but wanted to become the President. The retiring President, however, had seen through Goth's apparent desire for public service to his real lust for sheer power, and refused to nominate him as his successor. Burning with rage and frustration, Goth was easily subverted to the Master's service. Hiding his true motivations behind a façade of concern for justice, Goth attempted to have the Doctor swiftly executed for the murder of the President – the murder that Goth had, in fact, committed. When this failed, he allowed the Master to integrate him into the Matrix. There, he created a world of menace for the Doctor. Once again, however, Goth failed, and this time around the Master let Goth perish.

CASTELLAN SPANDRELL

Spandrell was the acid-tongued Castellan of the Time Lords. In charge of security, it became his duty to ferret out the truth about the murder of the President. Initially highly suspicious of the Doctor, he began to realize that the Doctor's theories were in fact making a good deal of sense. Less hide-bound than most Time Lords, he gave the Doctor sufficient freedom to either prove his accusations or to hang himself. In the end, his trust proved wise, and he aided the Doctor in fighting the plans of the Master.

COMMANDER HILRED

Hilred was the squad leader of the Chancellery Guard that failed to apprehend the Doctor when he arrived on Gallifrey. Much to Spandrell's disgust, Hilred proved incompetent in assignment after assignment. Hilred was simply incapable of taking any initiative, and unable to work out what was happening. Following orders, as usual, finally led to Hilred's death, when he attempted to staser the Master's 'body' and was killed by the archvillain.

CO-ORDINATOR ENGIN

Engin was in charge of the archive section of the Time Lords. Although his was normally a very sedentary role, he became involved with helping the Doctor and Spandrell to track down the stolen data extracts and the location of the Master's interference with the Matrix. To his own surprise, Engin found himself quite exhilarated by the whole affair. Though initially rather moribund, he rose to every challenge the Doctor gave him, and became very flexible and adaptable as the investigation went on.

RUNCIBLE

Runcible 'the Fatuous' was a contemporary of the Doctor's. He had a love for himself, his own abilities and his own worth that no one else shared. Verbose, posturing and foolish, he worked for the Public Video services, covering the retirement of the President. Borusa put him firmly in his place, which did little to abash Runcible. Later, while nervously aiding the Doctor in his investigation of the President's assassination, Runcible was slain by the Master.

Castellan Kelner with the Sontarans, to whom he betrayed Gallifrey (*The Invasion of Time*).

GOLD USHER

The Gold Usher is the Time Lord in charge of the ceremonial aspects of the Panopticon events. He is the spokesman for the traditions of Gallifrey, and responsible for the correct ordering of all ceremonies.

SOLIS

Solis was one of the Chancellery Guards.

TIME LORDS

Two other Time Lords were seen as they robed for the Panopticon resignation ceremony. Like many old men, they simply talked about the past, ignoring the history of the moment.

The Invasion of Time

CASTELLAN KELNER

Kelner was probably one of the most treacherous Time Lords ever to hold the exalted post as Castellan of the Citadel. When the Doctor arrived back on Gallifrey to claim his rightful place as the President, the oily Kelner was ever-helpful, and ready to betray all that he was supposed to hold dear. He weaseled his way (or so he thought) into the Doctor's confidence, and then proceeded to make the most of his new powers. He attempted to settle old scores, and seize as much power as he could. Despite his protestations or fidelity, Kelner planned to kill the Doctor and take over the reins of power himself. The Vardan invasion was stopped before Kelner could manage this, but when the Sontarans made their thrust, Kelner immediately betrayed his own race to the new invad-

Coordinator Engin, Castellan Spandrell and the fourth Doctor (*The Deadly Assassin*).

ers. Fawning to their every whim, he attempted to drop the transduction barriers for them, and constantly aided their efforts to capture or kill the Doctor. Finally, though, he fell into the hands of his fellow Time Lords that he had sought to betray, and was tried for his crimes.

ANDRED

Andred was a Commander of the Chancellery Guards, and a capable and resolute officer. He realized that the Doctor's methods of taking over Gallifrey, while ostensibly holding the post of President, were bad for the planet. While apparently obeying the Doctor, Andred began a revolutionary movement among the Guards to fight him. He aided the rebellious Time Lords as best he could, and when things seemed to be the most bleak, he tried to assassinate the Doctor for the good of Gallifrey. Luckily, he was outsmarted by the Doctor, who then managed to win him over to his camp in fighting the Vardans and Sontarans. Andred proved to be most effective, and he fought back on the side of the Doctor. After the threat to Gallifrey was eliminated, he and Leela settled down to get married.

GOMER

Gomer was the Surgeon General of the Time Lords, and responsible for the health of the President. When the Doctor collapsed during his inauguration, Gomer nursed him back to health.

SAVAR

Savar was one of the Time Lords that was deemed by Kelner to be 'dangerous' – mostly to him – and exiled from the Citadel.

THE GOLD USHER

The Gold Usher once again performed his ceremonial duties in the Panopticon.

RODAN

Rodan was a junior Time Lord assigned to very dull duties in the Space Control centre. It was her job to monitor approaching space traffic to Gallifrey – a pointless task, given the existence of the Transduction Barriers. She was so bored with her job that she allowed Leela in to talk with her, despite the fact that Leela was a wanted fugitive. Rodan was secure in her own arrogance – an arrogance that was soon eroded when she was forced to flee the Citadel into the wilderness with Leela. She simply could not fend for herself. Later, however, back inside the Citadel, she proved to be of invaluable aid to the Doctor when he was defending his TARDIS against the Sontarans. Under hypnosis, Rodan also constructed the Demat Gun for the Doctor to use.

NESBIN

Nesbin was the leader of the band of exiles now living in the wilderness outside the Citadel. He had formed a band of followers into an efficient and self-sufficient, if somewhat primitive, tribe. Leela managed to convince him and his followers to help the Doctor to fight the Vardan invasion.

ABLIF PRESTA JASKO

These three were members of Nesbin's band, who helped Leela and Rodan in the counter-attack on the Vardans.

CHANCELLERY GUARDS

These were members of the Guards led either by Andred or responsible directly to Kelner.

Arc of Infinity

HEDIN

Hedin was an old friend of the Doctor's, but one who had betrayed the Doctor because of his misguided

Presta and Nesbin (*The Invasion of Time*).

Hedin (*Arc of Infinity*).

loyalty to Omega. He revered what Omega had once been – apparently forgetting Omega's earlier attempts to destroy the Time Lords in *The Three Doctors* – and agreed whole-heartedly to help the renegade in his attempts to regain the material Universe. He stole the Doctor's Bio Data Extract, to help Omega fuse with the Doctor's body. He also betrayed the High Council – of which he was a member, all the time posing as a loyal friend to the Doctor. In the end, he died trying to stop the Time Lords from executing the Doctor and thus depriving Omega of the body he needed.

MAXIL

Maxil was a commander of the Chancellery Guard, a grim, humourless and sadistic person. Under the guise of merely doing his duty, Maxil enjoyed the inflicting of pain and humiliation on his charges. He was particularly looking forward to executing the Doctor. However, when he believed that this had been accomplished, he found less satisfaction in the act than he had expected.

Nyssa held by Chancellery guards as Commander Maxil surveys the stunned fifth Doctor (*Arc of Infinity*).

THE CASTELLAN

The Castellan was an efficient man – according to the Doctor's estimation, a trifle lacking in imagination – and intensely loyal. He was in charge of the security for the Citadel, and took this task very seriously. He was willing to sacrifice the Doctor in what he considered to be a good cause, and did not expect the Doctor to hold it against him. Later, in *The Five Doctors,* he was even willing to give the Master a pardon if he would help at a time of crisis. His basic failing was that he felt that the ends justified the means. Borusa agreed with this philosophy, and framed the Castellan for the theft and use of the Black Scrolls of Rassilon. He then had the Castellan murdered while he was 'attempting to escape'.

DAMON

Damon was another friend of the Doctor's, though apparently a very junior Time Lord. A technician in data services, he was astute enough to spot the theft of records and traced them. He helped Nyssa to save the Doctor, and proved both his friendship and intelligence in all that he did.

THALIA

Thalia was a high-ranking Time Lord and member of the High Council. Though duped by the actions of Hedin, she was usually clever enough. She sympathized with the Doctor's plight, but was willing to sacrifice his life in order to buy time for Gallifrey.

ZORAC

Zorac was the final member of the High Council of the Time Lords. Argumentative and unsettled, he sided against the Doctor in council, and agreed with the plan to execute him.

TALOR

Talor was a Time Lord computer supervisor, in charge of Damon. When the two of them spotted the theft of bio data, Talor reported it. He managed to get a trace on the theft, but was killed when he failed to be careful enough in his actions.

The Five Doctors

CHANCELLOR FLAVIA

Flavia was a high-ranking Time Lord on the Inner Council. She and the Castellan both agreed that the Master should be offered a pardon and a reward if he could help them fight the power drain that heralded the restarting of the Death Zone. After the Castellan's death she took over the command of the security forces, and backed the Doctor's plans. She arrived at the Dark Tower too late to help, and was left in temporary charge of Gallifrey while the Doctor took off on his travels once again.

Chancellor Flavia (*The Five Doctors*).

TECHNICIAN

This unnamed technician appeared only to receive brief orders from Borusa.

COMMANDER

The Commander of the Chancellery Guards arrested the Castellan on Borusa's orders. Borusa had already arranged a bribe for the man, and between the two of them they forced the Castellan to attempt to escape custody, allowing the Commander to shoot him down and kill him.

TIME LORDS

These three unnamed Time Lords were seen only in profile on the Tomb of Rassilon. They were three prior beings who had sought Rassilon's promise of immortality, and had been turned to stone. Borusa joined their numbers.

Petrified Time Lords (*The Five Doctors*).

The Ultimate Foe

THE KEEPER OF THE MATRIX

The Keeper of the Matrix was supposed to ensure that only authorized persons managed to gain access to the Matrix. A rigid and unimaginative person, he was completely out of his depth when both the Valeyard and the Master managed to gain access and take over the Matrix. In the end, the Valeyard managed to take over the Keeper's body and so escaped imprisonment in the Matrix.

The Keeper of the Matrix (*The Trial of a Time Lord*).

APPENDIX I:
THE
SCROLLS
OF
RASSILON

NOTE

What now follows is a rough translation of a series of recently-discovered scrolls. They are purported to have been written by Rassilon himself, and contain much new information about the formation of the Time Lords. These scrolls have been examined, and seem to be genuine; the paper, writing style and the claims made within them (as far as they can be checked) seem to bear out at least some of what is recorded within them.

However – and this is a very important point – what the scrolls contain is probably not strictly historical. For one thing, everything that was contained in the scrolls (save for the final entry) was written by Rassilon, and naturally only tells us of events from his own point of view. It must be always held in mind that Rassilon was primarily a politician, and a man with a vision. Accordingly, what he wrote may be considered either:

(1) The truth, as far as he could himself see it.

(2) An edited version of the true events. It may be that what follows is simply what Rassilon wanted posterity to know of what happened at the formation of the Time Lord society. Anything that deviated from his aims, therefore, would have either been deleted or seriously changed.

(3) A complete fabrication. With political aims in mind, Rassilon may have simply invented the whole tale. This last alternative seems unlikely, since he does record several incidents that do not reflect well on himself. This is not how Rassilon seems to have viewed the incidents in question,

however. And Rassilon must be credited with a very subtle and devious mind, and may in fact have added those derogatory episodes simply to give the document an air of verisimilitude.

Thus what follows may or may not be a true rendering of the origins of the Time Lords. While it does agree with all of the know facts about the Time Lords, it is possible that future discoveries may reveal errors, inconsistencies or even outright lies that may be contained within the scrolls.

Certain portions of the text have been edited out, merely for the sake of readability. Rassilon apparently felt compelled to justify his decisions, and often records long (and frequently dull) conversations with his contemporaries. To avoid boring the reader, these and certain technical details have been condensed or omitted entirely. Reasons for the omission of the technical passages must be obvious – they detail how to create and maintain many of the basic structures of the Time Lord civilization, and it is felt (at least by the Time Lords) that such knowledge must not be allowed to leave the security of their home world.

Finally, the original documents were dated, but in Old Gallifreyan. Since the old calendar of Gallifrey was abandoned shortly after the founding of the Panopticon, it is impossible to translate those dates at all. Hence they have simply been omitted. In their place, a rough numbering system has been added. It should be kept in mind, however, that the days, weeks and years on Gallifrey do not approximate well to any Earth periods.

THE
GALLIFREY
CHRONICLES

John Peel

DAY 1

My return to Gallifrey has given me the chance to examine the remnants of my fleet of bowships and the troops that manned them. The losses that we have suffered in the battle with the Vampire Horde have been staggering. Out of almost seven hundred bowships and sixteen thousand troops, only thirty-four ships and barely twelve hundred men have survived. It was a sad hour, watching the survivors stagger in like that, but it was also encouraging. Though tired – and in some cases almost lifeless – they still cheered me as I inspected their ships and condition before reporting to the High Council. With troops such as these, a man could do much if he so desired . . .

As usual, the High Council dithered and vacillated. They've known about the destruction of the Horde for three weeks, since I contacted them from the battlefront. In that time, they have made only one firm decision, and it's an appalling one. They tell me that the public mood has been turned against warfare, and want me to dismiss the entire Chancellery Guard now that the blood-letting is over.

If I were not so used to their hypocrisy and mealy-mouthed stupidity, their decision would have infuriated me. These troops are all that are left of the brave men and women who set out to save the entire Galaxy from the most deadly scourge imaginable, and the High Council wants simply to pat them on the back and disband them. They believed me, however, when I assured them that I would do my best to implement their wishes.

Fools and cowards that they are, they deserve what will come to them. Pandak especially – as President, he should have more sense than to allow himself to be carried away on any wave of public sentiment.

I do not blame the general populace for this wish to end war. I, too, would like to see its necessity vanish. But as a practical man, I know that this is impossible until we of High Gallifrey are much stronger than now . . .

DAY 3

I spoke at length with General Gimel who assures me that the troops are doing well. They have all been billeted, as I suggested, in the Citadel. Pandak readily accepted my story that this was in order to have them all together for processing and discharge. Gimel reports that most of the wounded are now on the road to recovery. My plans are beginning finally to coalesce . . .

Omega was somewhat surprised to see me. Apparently, the High Council hadn't considered it worthwhile to tell him of my return. Typical. Still, he was glad to see me, and I even more glad to hear his news. He showed me around his new laboratory with a great show of pride and optimism. Despite the man's ego, he remains one of the most gifted cyber-technicians I have ever known, and probably one of the four or five most brilliant minds Gallifrey has ever produced.

His masterpiece of engineering is now nearing the final stages. Before I left on the campaign, I had stressed to him the necessity of keeping the details secret from the High Council, and thankfully he has done so. Their latest talk of peace in our time would really turn rancid in their mouths if they could see what he has – with his usual lack of modesty – called the Hand of Omega.

'A fist,' he said, laughing. 'One that will tighten about any star we aim it at. A fist that will clench and crush the life force of the star, and create an instant supernova.'

With a cheerful heart, I congratulated him on his progress. The prototype has been hooked into the computers, and simulator tests can begin within the month. When we have such a solar activator for our arsenal, there will be no planet that will ever dare challenge Gallifrey's supremacy. Who would dare, knowing that with one such device we could snuff out their sun in an instant, and doom them to either the flames of a massive supernova or else the lingering death of utter cold?

My plans are coming together even better than I had dared to hope...

DAY 7

For the first time, doubt has entered my mind. Oh, not about my plans – they are all in place and proceeding beautifully. In just a short while, I shall be ready to move. No, the problem lies in another area entirely.

He breezed into my offices inside the Citadel today. How he had managed to get inside the building to begin with he would not say, but it seems that the man has a signed pass! Wanting simply to have him arrested, I demanded his papers, and he handed over a special pass, signed by me!

Yet I know full well that I have never signed such a pass for this person.

Infuriatingly, he pointed out that the pass is genuine, and that it was indeed, signed by me. He was quite correct – the ink and sigil are kept locked in my office at all times, and they were correctly affixed to the pass. I demanded to know how he had acquired it, but he only smiled.

'When you know *how* I got it,' he told me, with incredible cheek, 'then I can tell you *why* I am here. But not until then.'

I was more than tempted simply to have him taken to the roof and pushed off, but until I know who he is, how he obtained that pass, and who he works for, I dare do nothing drastic. Gimel favours using the mind probe on the man, but I seriously doubt it would work. If the man is an enemy's agent, then he will either resist the beam or die under it. If he is not an enemy, then I cannot afford to antagonise a friend. In the end, I had him escorted under strict guard to a guest suite. The man smiled as he left; apparently he had expected me to make just such a move.

He worries me. Not badly enough to halt my plans – I doubt that they could be halted now even if I tried – but he does trouble me. Who is he? And what is his purpose for being here? I cannot explain it, but I feel that there is something of great significance in his arrival.

DAY 8

I spent a sleepless night worrying about that confounded intruder, but I am still unable to know what to make of him. Still, I was able to force my worries into the background, for there is still much to be done. My own experimental staff has continued with my research while I was away, and Jelen informs me that the generators are being set up now. They will be located at the heart of the Citadel, close to the main security level. Gimel's men have unobtrusively taken over the task of guarding the building, allowing the High Council's men to go and join in the general revelry that seems to have infected the planet.

I watched some of the festivities on Public Access Video. The foolishness of the average man or woman appals me. There they were, literally dancing in the streets, making idiots of themselves, and getting drunk all because we had won the war against the vampires. Pandak made some sort of speech about that being the final war, and how soon we would be able to usher in an age of peace such as Gallifrey had never known.

I have to give the old moron his due – he can make a rousing speech. Well, he should be able to – he's done nothing but make speeches for almost fifty years. Others of us have had better things to do with our time. I was musing over his latest ramblings when the stranger turned up again. He had somehow managed to give the guards the slip, and made his way into my office!

'Ironic, isn't it?' he commented, gesturing at the screen. 'Pandak never spoke truer words – an age of peace indeed. Pity he doesn't know it'll be your peace and not his.'

I felt a chill pass through me. 'What are you talking about?' I demanded.

'Have you worked out where I got that pass from?' was all he would say. The guards arrived and dragged him out of my office, but he had already done what he had come to do – he had unsettled me yet again.

How much does this mysterious man know of my plans? And what does he intend to do about them? Surely if he had intended to reveal them to Pandak and the Council, he would not now be here. And Gimel is no help. His staff have checked the computer records through three times, and find absolutely no record of this man anywhere, under any name . . .

But I have other worries. My plans for Gallifrey are known to no one but myself. I find myself longing for a confidant to trust, someone who could succeed me. There is always the possibility that my plans will not work, and that I may die in the attempt. In that case, to have a worthy successor would be a great relief. But to whom could I entrust this task? No. For now at least, I must remain alone in what I know.

DAY 10

Now that it has begun, it seems somehow to be anticlimactic.

Gimel led the Chancellery Guard on the raid at dawn. The High Council was still sleeping off their collective hangovers when the men arrested them. Apparently Castellan Temus was the only one to even reach for a weapon. There's not enough left of him to make it worthwhile holding a funeral. The other four, including that idiot Pandak, are all in cells in the Panopticon chambers.

The Transduction Barriers are in full force about Gallifrey, sealing all aliens out – and all Gallifreyans in. The second level of the Barriers has been established about the Citadel, and no one can now enter or leave without my permis-

sion. Not that I expect any problems from the people of Gallifrey. They are sheep, all ready to bleat and cry, but not to take any kind of positive action, especially if they should spot a wolf. So far, probably no one knows of the abduction of the Council, but it cannot remain a secret for long. The existence of the Transduction Barriers will take them a little longer to discover, but it must be done gradually. They must be on the verge of panic for my plan to work.

The four surviving members of the Council – Pandak, the Lady Norin, Zabor and Mayeron – were alternatively incensed and afraid. After letting them stew in their own imaginations for several hours, I finally had them brought to me. Pandak tried his usual bluster, and I let him blather on for about five minutes before I nodded to Gimel. He tapped his staser significantly, and Pandak's whining cut off short.

'I now control Gallifrey,' I told them bluntly. 'The Chancellery Guard are, thanks to your own edicts, the only armed force still in existence on the planet. They will remain that way. They are, as you can see, quite loyal only to Gimel and myself. And they have very little desire to be legislated out of their jobs by you.'

Predictably, one of them – Zabor – blurted out: 'You can't get away with this! The people—'
'Will do nothing,' I answered. 'First, they are not, for the most part, armed. The Guard is, and has orders to kill anyone trying to get to us here. Second, there is a Barrier up about the entire fortress, so that even with weapons the people could not get in. Third, the general population of Gallifrey couldn't give a damn who rules them, as long as it is done well, and causes them as little personal inconvenience as possible. Fourth –' I smiled. 'Fourth, I will tell you later.'

'Tell them now,' broke in an excruciatingly familiar voice. It was the stranger once again, blithely walking into the private conference as though he had every right to be there! 'Or shall I tell them about the Transduction Barriers?'

How he knew about them was beyond me, but

I had to find out just how much he did know. I suggested that he tell the Council. He did exactly that.

'Rassilon has set up an impenetrable force-field about the planet. It's very effective, and may well prove to be quite deadly.'

So he had grasped my plan! I allowed him to continue talking. The Council, of course, did not understand what he was saying, so he spelled it out for them: 'Rassilon is one of the greatest force-field engineers this Universe has ever known. The Transduction Barriers can keep out everything outside Gallifrey.'

Mayeron blinked, helplessly. 'A good defence,' he finally said.

'You don't understand,' he replied, with more patience than I could have mustered. 'I mean *everything* out – including, if he wants to, the sun's rays.'

That finally sank in! I smiled at their expressions of horror. 'As our guest has surmised,' I admitted, 'such a level is possible. I do not think that I shall have any trouble from the general populace when at a stroke I can condemn them all to freeze to death – do you?'

'You would never dare!' Lady Norin stormed. 'Even you could not be so callous as to condemn a planet to death.'

I was afraid that they might take it like that. Drawing my staser from the desk drawer, I held it loosely in one hand. 'Believe me,' I assured them, 'I am quite capable of doing what is needed. If there is any one of you who thinks I would hesitate for a second to kill if I have to, they may now speak up.' I raised the staser. 'I will use their corpse to demonstrate that I am in earnest about this.'

That shut them all up, quickly. It's one thing to talk about death in general terms, but quite another to stare into the face of Death and feel its fingers about your heart.

'Good,' I smiled. 'Now we've settled that point, I think that it's high time we began work, don't you?'

'What are you talking about?' Zabor asked.

Pandak cut him short. 'It's obvious,' he sighed. 'This maniac has some plan in mind in which we must play some part. Otherwise we would already be dead.'

He wasn't quite as senile as I had thought. 'Excellent,' I complimented him. 'So, to details: Gallifrey is, effectively, mine. However, if I were to simply go onto Public Access Video and announce this fact, then it might cause a little...'

'Riot?' the stranger suggested.

'Unpleasantness,' I corrected. 'So what I would like you four to do is to make the announcement for me. Nothing grand, just something along the lines of handing in your resignations and passing over the Government to the hero of the War with the Vampires. You may, if you wish, embellish the picture a little – but it had better be in a positive way. If it is, then you will all be allowed to retire to your estates in South Gallifrey.'

'And how do we know you won't simply have us executed to avoid trouble?' Mayeron growled.

'Because that won't be necessary,' I sighed. 'Once you are outside the Citadel, the only way you can ever get back in is if I allow it. I really can't imagine any scenario that might make me do that. As for your stirring up trouble among the people – well, that wouldn't be very clever. They, too, are trapped outside the Citadel, and I am immune to anything that they may seek to do. The only reason that I need you to make your broadcast is to prevent unnecessary panic and the inevitable accompaniment of bloodshed. If you truly do care about the people of Gallifrey – which, to be honest, I seriously doubt – you'll see that the best thing that you can do for them is to calm matters down. On the other hand, if you care at all for your own miserable hides, I assure you that the only way you will leave the Citadel alive is to do as I wish and make that broadcast.'

The stranger broke in once again. 'Allow me to assure you that Rassilon is perfectly right. He's holding the winning hand here, and things will be a lot smoother if you do as he asks.'

'And who are you?' Pandak demanded. 'One of his lackeys?'

'Oh, no, nothing of the sort,' he answered. 'I'm a sort of – travelling consultant. I've a strong line in good advice, and my advice to you is to play along with Rassilon here.'

'We will think about it,' Pandak agreed, mustering all the dignity he could.

'Take time,' I said. 'Take as much as five hours. But no more.' They were led away to their cells again, and I returned to my real problem. He flashed me a cheerful smile.

'So,' I said, 'what am I to make of you?'

'Oh, pretty much what I told them,' he replied, airily. 'I have a very good line in advice.'

'And you have some for me?'

'Plenty, Rassilon.' Suddenly serious, he glared at me. 'But there is no point in my giving it to you until you work out how I got that pass.' He smiled at the remaining Guards. 'Would you like to take me back to my cell now?'

An infuriating person! But what am I to do with him? Strangely, I do not feel that he holds any malice for me, but it is equally clear that he disapproves of what I am doing. I cannot help but feel that the key to my future lies within his grasp.

In some ways, I wish that I could trust him. He seems to have a brilliant mind, and he would make a worthy successor to me – when I am ready either to retire or to die.

DAY 15

Since the 'resignation' speech by the High Council, things have been going well. Oh, there has been plenty of speculation in the news and gossip all over the planet, I am certain, as to what it means. But, on the whole, my revolution has been surprisingly bloodless. I had expected a few thousand casualties at the very least, and in the end only twenty-seven people have died. A small price to pay to gain the mastery of the planet.

I have begun to make my reforms now. Though I am certain that the High Council views me as simply a megalomaniac with a lust for power and a lucky invention that enabled me to seize control, I know that this is simply due to their own foolish limitations. When Gimel let them all free, they could not believe it. They had expected a knife in the back, and probably will go on expecting sudden death in the night for the rest of their stupid lives. They truly cannot grasp the enormity of my plans. Even Gimel, for all his loyalty, has no concept of my aims. Only Omega and – once again! – the stranger seem to be able to grasp anything of what I am planning.

I suspect that I am going to have trouble sooner or later with Omega. A brilliant scientist, but it turns out that the man is secretly a democrat. He actually believes that all political power should be derived from the people. What an idiot! As if they could possibly know what is best for them, and that by taking a count of hands, it should come to pass. I told him that democracy is the illusion that all people are equal when it is perfectly apparent that they are not. Am I to be compared to some snivelling little fool, barely out of school, and with no experience in life, and no ambition other than to earn himself a comfortable living, raise a few brats, and then spend his life watching The Games on the Video? Why ever should we be considered of equal worth?

Needless to say Omega could not answer me, but I doubt I've dispelled his foolish faith in that

asinine process. Well, I care little for what he may think, just as long as he does what he alone can do.

DAY 23

Finally, the Hand of Omega is finished! According to all of the computer simulations, it should work perfectly, but we still have the field test to go, of course. Once we have this weapon, there will be nothing to stand between Gallifrey and total security. Any world that would disagree with us would have its sun annihilated!

It is difficult for me to contain my excitement. I have been looking forward so long to this point that even that *he* cannot ruin my good humour.

Yes, he still manages to get about as he wishes. I've finally dismissed the guards I had assigned to watch him, since he manages to elude them whenever he pleases. And I retain my belief that he is not really dangerous. At least, not in any physical sense. The man has a fierce intelligence that may well be the most dangerous unleashed force in the Universe. But I am not afraid of this – if I cannot contain it, then I can simply have him killed at any moment, and he's too intelligent not to realize this. I cannot fathom him at all, and he won't talk until I tell him the answer to that stupid riddle of his about the pass! As if I have nothing better to do with my time than to work out a puzzle!

The question that vexes me at the moment is which star to select to test the Hand of Omega on. Not one too close to Gallifrey – I have no desire to flood the planet with radiation. Nor one too far away to be seen. The people of Gallifrey must be able to look up into the sky and see the evidence of our new place in the scheme of things! Given the speed of light, the choice must be of a star probably within six or seven light years from us. Any further, then there will be too long a gap between triggering the supernova and in seeing the effects in the night sky.

This is where I am at a loss, because all of the stars that fall into this band have planetary groups, and at least one habitable planet in each system. Not that I would hesitate to destroy a nascent civilization if it becomes necessary, but it does seem a waste when a dead system would make just as great a mark. It is simply a matter of deciding which of the twelve planets has the least potential, I expect.

DAY 26

Really, he can be most infuriating!

I had finally decided upon destroying the star Ezmion VI when he burst in on me, unannounced as usual, and started to berate me for the choice. Finally – and, I feel, justifiably – annoyed, I threw the sheet of names at him. 'Then you decide which one to destroy,' I told him.

He tore the list into shreds and literally jumped on the pieces. 'There is no need to destroy anyone!' he yelled at me. 'Omega's device works! Why waste lives proving it?'

'We are both practical men.' I said patiently. 'We know that the device works, but there are going to be plenty of people who will never believe that it can detonate a star until they see it done. We have to blow one up to prove that we have the power.'

'A weapon must be seen to be effective,' he growled.

'Exactly.'

'Then choose a dead star. Polyphilos.' He stabbed a finger at the chart on my desk. 'Nothing could ever live there.'

'Polyphilos?' His suggestion had never occurred to me. Omega – who had sat silently through the discussion until now – leaned forward. 'But that's a Q star,' he objected. 'It's highly unstable to begin with.'

'And totally out of the question,' I added.

'First, because it's unstable, who would believe that we had destroyed it, and it hadn't simply blown itself up? And, second, it lies twenty-six light years away. I am not going to wait almost three decades to prove my power. We do not have the time to waste.'

'Time,' Omega mused, staring at the chart. 'Time!' he cried, leaping to his feet, and running out of the room. I stared after him in amazement.

'He's gone crazy,' I finally said.

'No,' the stranger corrected me. 'He's gone sane. I can only trust that you will go just as sane. Rassilon – give me three days. Three days. What's that to wait for the test?'

I sighed. 'Very well. Three days. Then I destroy Ezmion VI.'

DAY 29

Well, I have finally made either the greatest decision of my entire career or the greatest blunder that will be known in all of recorded history.

I have given Omega permission to use Polyphilos as his target.

I'm not sure I can follow all of his calculations, but if he is correct, then we shall have even greater power than even I had ever dreamed of. Gallifrey will be secure for all of time.

He came rushing in here this morning, a pile of calculations a foot thick in his hands, and so excited he could not speak. Finally, he calmed down enough to explain his crazy theory.

'It's the Q star that makes it possible,' he explained. 'Tremendous potential energy, locked into a tight field because of the axial spin of the star. If we detonate Polyphilos, then we can actually channel that power.'

He showed me his calculations. Some I shall have to take his word on, but others made more than perfect sense to me. What his new idea boils down to basically is this: if we use the Hand of Omega to detonate the Q star, the resulting explosion of energy can be captured and utilized. It will produce a sort of one-directional explosion, which Omega proposes to aim at Gallifrey. The force of detonation will turn the star into a source of chronons.

Chronons are the basic particles of time. Using these, we can then contain the explosion, stretching it out quite literally forever, and producing a continuous flow of energy directed towards Gallifrey, a flow consisting of high-energy chronons.

I have to confess that I didn't see the point in all of this initially, but Omega has it all worked out. Given the proper force fields to shield us from the power, and a collection device here on Gallifrey itself, the chronon particles will allow us to penetrate through time itself.

The Time Scoop used to collect the players in the Game does this, of course, but in a very crude manner. It uses taranium for the process, and we are fortunate in having a large supply of the rare metal on our closest moon. But it's a very rough process, and works only over a small area.

Using the harnessed force of the Q star, however, we will be able to be much, much more selective. Omega hypothesizes that we should be able not merely to pull objects and people out of time, but also be able to push them through from here to any time or place in the Universe in a single instant! We would be able to manipulate time, instead of being a prey to its implacable forces.

The thought appeals to me greatly, and I have given Omega the permissions and funds he needs to complete the process. I shall have to design the force-field generators and equipment myself for the containment fields here, and for our use when we detonate Polyphilos. After all, if we were caught in the explosion, who knows what might happen to us? Perhaps

we should simply be eradicated in a microsecond. But, given the strange forces at work in the heart of a Q star, perhaps something even worse might occur . . .

And, of course, should the collectors for the beamed power not be perfectly aligned on Gallifrey, then the flood of chronons that hits the planet will literally explode it, and send its scattered fragments throughout all of eternity.

We shall have either the staggering power to manipulate time and space on a scale undreamed of, or else the biggest explosion in history since the creation of the Universe itself.

What scientist could resist a challenge like that?

DAY 34

Putting a stop to the Games is probably the most unpleasant task I have ever had to face in my short time in power. Oh, the populace of Gallifrey grumbled about the higher taxes I imposed, and they complained when I insisted on funding pure research, but nothing like this protest! When I imposed the strict segregation in schooling, there were protests for days! The parents complained that I was unfairly rewarding brighter children, and that intelligence couldn't be measured in academic marks and all of the usual liberal claptrap. You cannot argue with people like that, and I didn't bother. I don't care if they think I'm sending a message to the lower classes that they are not worth as much as the brighter children. The future will lie in the hands of those with ability and talents, not in the hands of the masses.

Even General Gimel thinks my decision to ban the Games, however, is a bad move. I do not question his loyalty, of course, but sometimes his blunt soldier's opinions are a bit too much for me to stomach.

'You can institute all the reforms you like,' he told me in private. 'It doesn't matter how un-

popular they are, if they produce results, the complaints will stop. Your education policies might be controversial, but if they lead to an increase in output and revenues generally, then protest will die down. But stopping the Games is madness. They are the outlet for the masses – they funnel their emotions and anger and fury into watching the combatants. It's therapeutic for them.'

'I don't much care what it is for them,' I replied. 'If the Time Scoop is still operating when we explode Polyphilos, the time distortion that it produces could wreck the careful system of forces that I am setting up.'

'Well, if you must shut it down, do so only when you really have to.'

'Gimel,' I answered, wishing he had the brain to understand me, 'time distortions aren't something that die down in an hour or two. The ripples from the Scoop could last for years for all we know. I have to have it turned off now so that I can definitely know what effects it has had on the time aura about Gallifrey. Don't you understand that if my calculations are wrong, then this entire planet will be less than dust floating in the vacuum of space?'

'If it's that dangerous,' he growled, 'then maybe you shouldn't even attempt it.'

'Gimel, don't be short-sighted. Exploding a Q star is a theoretical possibility that might occur to any civilization that has broken through time in any manner whatsoever. Right now, we are the only civilization that we know has done this. Sooner or later, there will be others. If one of them should harness a Q star, then they will be able to control all of time and space and the destinies of a myriad worlds – including ours. Do you not see that if we fail to conquer time, then whichever race does so will also conquer us? Now that we know it can be done, it must be done, for the security of Gallifrey.'

That he could finally understand. He was good at any kind of logic that involved war. 'But the banning of the Games will be a hard blow.'

'We all must make sacrifices, Gimel,' I told him. 'The populace will have to find another way to sate their bloodlust and boredom?'

'And if it is on each other?' he asked. 'There are groups who claim that without the sublimated violence of the Games, we shall have an increase in crime, particularly violent crime.'

'Then let them take it out on one another,' I told him. 'Violence is the first home of the foolish man. And his last.' I smiled. 'We should organize special patrols, then, and arm them. Give those who want to the chance physically to fight back if there's an increase in crime. That should make them happy. They can kill one another off.'

'And a lot of innocent people,' Gimel objected.

He was getting tiresome. 'Innocence is a word that means whatever its user wants. Being born means you're involved in life. There are no innocents – merely the uncommitted. We are going to ban the Games, and if the people object, let them. They will sooner or later find some other stupid diversion to take their minds off that one. If it does become a problem, then we shall act. Otherwise, let them complain.'

DAY 38

Well, Gimel was certainly right about the complaints! Morning, noon and night, days without let-up. I finally agreed to see a group representing the most vocal complaints. Their leader got right to the point, demanding that the Games be restarted, or else.

'Or else what?' I asked, curiously.

'We are ready to organize planetwide strikes,' he answered, with stupid pride. 'Bring everything to a halt until you give in.'

'And what makes you think I would ever give in?' I wanted to know.

'You would have to,' he told me. 'Civilization would begin to crumble.'

'Your civilization, not mine,' I told him. 'The only people you would affect by this strike of yours would be yourselves and your families. I couldn't care less what you do amongst yourselves, to be honest. I'm tempted to allow you to go ahead. However, I have had a better idea.'

'What's that?' he asked, suspiciously.

'I'll revive a form of the Games,' I told him. 'Only, instead of it being played using alien warriors, it would be played using whiners, complainers, malcontents and the like. You, for example. You want the Games so badly, then you play in them. You fight, and bleed and die for the entertainment of your fellow sociopaths. Don't you find it morally repugnant to kidnap intelligent beings from other worlds and force them to fight one another to the death just to give you something to watch with your supper? Or are words like morality and decency too complicated for you to understand? If so, I will make it plain. Tell your members that the Games will recommence next week. The first matches will be played out using the ten people whose names I first hear of complaining about the loss of the Games.'

'You can't do that!' he screamed, furious. 'You cannot use a citizen of Gallifrey as a pawn in the Games.'

'You idiot!' I snapped back at him. 'I can do whatever I chose to do. And I swear to you that I shall do exactly what I've told you. Starting now, anyone who protests the loss of the Games goes into the Forbidden Zone to play in the next round. Do any of you have anything to say to that?'

Gimel and his Guards moved significantly closer. The delegation paled to a man, and no one spoke.

'Good. I see that we understand one another

perfectly. Now, go home, and make certain that everyone understands what I have just told you. In two days' time, I shall have written into law that anyone who publicly calls for the return of the Games will be fighting in them the next day.'

I suspect that the fuss of the cancellation will die down very quickly now.

DAY 43

It is really quite astonishing how much progress has been made in so short a time. The public outcry over the cancellation of the Games has died down once everyone realized that my threat was quite serious. It took only one round-up of the dissident factions to convince people that they didn't really want the Games back after all.

I was tempted to dismantle the entire apparatus for the Time Scoop and to obliterate the playing arena, but realized in time that this would have simply been operating out of spite. Instead, I simply set up a new force field generator within the Great Tower – of which only I know the frequency – and have sealed off the entire Forbidden Zone. The apparatus for the Time Scoop I had moved, and it is now well hidden within the walls of the redesigned Panopticon section of the Citadel.

Finally, I am getting the chance to indulge in my architectural leanings. I have been rebuilding the Citadel. I am, perhaps, an idealist, but I am no fool. Though I know all of my legislation is necessary to make Gallifrey strong, I do not for one moment imagine that I am popular because of it. I very much doubt whether it would be safe for me to leave the Citadel for a few years yet, and am thus making a virtue out of necessity. With the Citadel building as my basis, I am redesigning the entire complex. Once it is finished, all the power – both intellectual as well as physical – on the planet will be concentrated here. I plan an Academy area, the Panopticon itself, which will house all the rep-

resentatives of the various Chapters (as soon as I am certain that I can trust them, of course), the Security offices, to replace the rather cramped quarters that Gimel and the Guards now occupy, and the various laboratories and public offices that are needed. I am also adding a Presidential suite or two. Though it is too soon yet, I shall eventually have to accept the office of President, although not until I am certain that I can trust enough people to form the remainder of the High Council. Until then, I will stand alone.

DAY 50

Some obscure biologist by the name of Thremix (poor fellow, being saddled with a name like that!) came to see me today with what must be one of the most extraordinary ideas for a project that I have ever approved. Since the proclamation about the new funding for pure science, I have sat through quite a number of odd sessions, either to approve or deny funding, but Thremix was certainly one of the strangest petitioners I have met yet.

He proposes to develop a disease called immortality!

'Not a disease, exactly,' he corrected me in his nervous way when I laughed. 'A virus. It will live within the body, and breed. It will be specifically tied into the genes of the person it inhabits, and will constantly monitor that person's body, eliminating and repairing anything that goes wrong. For example, if you were to break a leg, it would enable the break to heal in about a quarter of the time that it would naturally. Burns, diseases and other problems could be healed in a day.'

'And death?' I asked, half-believing him; he was so intense and serious.

'That, actually, it couldn't do much about. Not real death, that is.'

'Are there any other kinds?' Gimel asked, in

his brusque way.

'Oh, yes. Suppose, for a moment, that you had a heart attack, and collapsed. Would you die?'

'Not if there was a physician around who could restart my heart,' Gimel answered. 'If I was alone – yes, I'd probably die.'

'Well, my virus would be like a surgeon, only an internal one. It would restart your heart for you, because it would know how your body should be functioning, and work to keep it like that. Of course, if you had a complete breakdown of your body system, then it couldn't work. For instance, if someone shot you with a staser.'

'That's a relief,' Gimel said, with his grim humour. 'I like to see a man I shoot stay dead.'

I have to confess I was intrigued by Thremix's suggestions. Mad as they might seem, he did sound serious, and he wanted a pitifully small amount of money. He almost slobbered over me in gratitude when I agreed to fund him, but I finally got rid of him. I could see that Gimel didn't approve, so I invited his comments.

'I had the man checked out,' he told me. 'He's considered completely unreliable by the scientific community. A charlatan.'

'Good,' I replied. 'So was I, at one time. And think, Gimel – if he is right in even one half of what he claims, then we shall have solved a problem I had thought unsurmountable. I'm sure you have the same trouble I have. Have you ever given serious thought to who will succeed you when you either retire or die?'

'I've six or seven men I've had my eye on, Lord Rassilon,' he said. 'But, frankly – well, none of them is exactly what I had hoped for.'

'Well, you can imagine my problem. Gallifrey is running smoothly with my hand at its political helm, but if I were to die it would undoubtedly founder back into its stupid old ways. But one day I must die, and pass on the reins of power. I am constantly tormented by the night-mare that I might chose the wrong man, someone who will dilute my dream, or prove to be weak or corrupt.

'Now, if Thremix should be correct, we can take a lot longer to make our decisions. Perhaps they might even be indefinitely postponed. And if he is wrong, what have we lost? A little money. I think the chance is worth taking.'

Gimel was not convinced, I could see, but he wisely held his counsel.

DAY 73

Thremix finally resurfaced today, with news that is both good and bad. Despite Gimel's misgivings, the biosynthesist has produced some results. He's managed to create his strain of virus and he is fairly certain that it will do what he wants. There are, however, a few drawbacks to his wonderful invention.

'I can't guarantee that it will work on everyone,' he explained. 'Theoretically, there are some problems. There are three possibilities that I can see. First, it will work perfectly, and the recipient will become endowed with extra virtues and a terrific resistance to sickness, ageing and even death itself. That's the best-case scenario. 'Second, the recipient's own bodily defences will think it is an infection, and try to combat it. In this case, the virus might simply be overwhelmed, and the recipient will be left as he was before the infection. Alternatively, the virus might win, and take effect. It's impossible to be certain what would happen there.

'Third, what I am really worried about! My virus takes its template for rebuilding the body and keeping it healthy when we inject it into the body. But what if the first cell it chances to scan is actually a diseased cell? Or a parasite, or some other defective cell? It will assume that this is the normal cell, and wreck the rest of the body to try to match it. It would become a killer instead of a healer.'

'Interesting,' I agreed. 'Is there any way for

you to predict which will happen with any given person?'

'Oh, yes,' he told me. 'That's simply a matter of taking a small tissue sample, and injecting it with the virus. If the sample dies, then so would the recipient.'

'Then why not simply inject only those who could stand the treatment?'

'You don't seem to grasp the problem fully,' Thremix said, in some anguish. 'My process is a virus. I can't simply inject one person or another with it and leave it at that. It will breed like any normal virus and spread from person to person as contact is made. If even one person contracts the virus, within a month the entire planet would become infected.'

I began to see his problem. 'Well, I think you'd better try refining it a bit.'

He shrugged. 'I really can't see how I could do much else with it,' he admitted. 'There are limits to what you can do with a simple virus.'

A dreadful thought came to me. 'Just a moment. This business of infection. Let's say, for the sake of argument, that you injected yourself with the virus. I take it that you haven't?'

'Of course not!' he said in horror. 'I've used only experimental animals, in strict quarantine.'

'Good, well, if you were to pass on the virus to, say, Gimel here, wouldn't it simply kill him? After all, his genetic code is entirely different to yours, and the virus would assume it was all faulty.' I could see that the idea didn't appeal much to Gimel.

'No, I compensated for that,' Thremix explained. 'The virus works only if the genetic variations are of a small order. Say, up to twenty per cent. If there's more than that, then it takes a fresh sample and starts again. So if

another person were infected with the virus, the little devil would simply recalibrate, so to speak, and start to work.'

'Another problem occurs to me,' Gimel put in, showing more sense than I had expected of him. 'How would it affect a pregnant woman? Would it assume that the baby's genetic coding is wrong, and alter it to an exact duplicate of the mother's?'

'Ah, that had occurred to me,' Thremix admitted. 'I, too, had that same vision – a future populated purely by women, each one identical in all aspects to their mother. Until, of course, all the men capable of breeding with them died out, dooming the race to eventual extinction. Not a pretty thought, is it? Fortunately, the virus is sophisticated enough to allow for that. I can ensure that a baby – with fifty per cent of the mother's genetic material – would be considered as a secondary unit. You see, it's simply a variation on the infection problem.'

'So, basically, you're telling me that we have only one choice to make,' I asked him. 'Either to infect the whole planet with the longevity virus or to withhold it from all.'

'Exactly,' he agreed. 'We must do one or the other. It's not a decision I would relish making.'

'It's not a decision that you have to make,' I told him, coldly. 'I shall have to decide.'

'It might be wise, in either case,' Gimel suggested, 'to have Thremix here test out the virus on samples from the top level of command. It would be unfortunate if any of us proved to have an adverse reaction.'

I could see his point there! Naturally, I have ordered a series of tests to be conducted among the people I can trust. Especially, of course, on myself. If the virus will kill me, then it will stay hidden away until I am dead. If it will not work, the same is to hold true. If, on the other hand, it will work on me, then I really have no option but to authorize its release.

DAY 80

Thremix has returned with some good news and some excellent news. It turns out that in his usual silly way, it had never occurred to him to perform tests on a humanoid subject. He confined his work to lower animal life. What he has found is truly remarkable, though perhaps somewhat accidental.

The virus not merely heals, but regenerates tissue. Portions of diseased or dismembered tissues, even ones that were decades old, actually grew back into place. He's off again, now, working on some new thoughts that this has given to him, and with my blessing. Perhaps his virus will prove to be even better than I dared to ever have hoped.

And the excellent news is that the virus will work perfectly on both myself and Gimel.

DAY 84

I am beginning to suspect that a little of Omega's egocentricity is rubbing off onto me. My personal force shields are finished, and work – as I expected – perfectly. They are worn across the shoulders, and because of their appearance, I have named them the Sashes of Rassilon. Omega smiled when I handed his over to him. Well, if he can name his invention after his hand, he needn't be so amused with my names!

Still, both Sashes work perfectly, allowing us to approach within the critical distance that we shall need to penetrate when we detonate Polyphilos. Omega has worked brilliantly on his engineering, and only two ships are required to do the work. He will man the main ship, which will dive into the corona of the star and deliver the Hand of Omega with precisely the right trajectory it will need. I had wondered about this, since the Hand is capable of remote programming, but Omega had his reasons.

'If we just wanted to detonate the star, then I could fire off the Hand from here,' he agreed. 'But we need to detonate it at a specific instant in its rotation, so as to funnel the chronons on an exact path. That requires us to approach within two solar radii of the star. Your ship will maintain the main force fields in place, and mine will dive in to deliver the Hand precisely on target. These Sashes will protect us from the forces, and then we can return to the main fleet, which will be holding an orbital pattern much farther out.'

There is no doubt at all in my mind that the man is a genius. Which makes him doubly dangerous, of course, because he has never hidden from me the fact that he thinks I should share the reins of power with elected officials.

I shall have to ensure that he is watched.

DAY 85

Once again, Gimel has proven his resourcefulness. I had mentioned the thought about watching Omega, and Gimel informed me that he's had an agent close to Omega for many weeks now. Gimel, careful as ever, has never fully trusted Omega. He has also taken it upon himself to have other individuals monitored, including Thremix, it seems. That strikes me as going too far. Thremix hasn't got a single political thought in his head. I seriously doubt if he even dreams of anything that doesn't have viruses in it.

Still, it makes me think – with all of this surveillance, none of which I knew about before, how much can Gimel himself be trusted?

DAY 98

Now that I've worked it out, I suppose it should have occurred to me before. Still, the idea was so preposterous that I'm not surprised that it took me this long to arrive at the correct answer. I now know where the stranger got his

pass from.

I gave it to him. Today, in fact, in my office.

He looked at it, and then put it away in one of those baggy pockets of his.

'I knew you'd realize eventually,' he said.

'It was the only explanation that made sense,' I agreed, modestly. 'The only way you could get a legitimate pass was to obtain it from me. Since I hadn't given you one in the past, it had to be in the future. Then it all made sense. Tell me – who exactly are you?'

'I suppose you might call me a Time Lord, Rassilon. One of the people that you are in the process of creating.'

'You are the result of my plans?' I studied his appearance with unavoidable dismay. He looks so much like a tramp!

'Well, something like me, at any rate,' he conceded. 'I am considered to be something of a maverick.'

'And the rest of your people?'

'Oh, terribly serious and dull. You'd love them. A place for everything, and everything in its time. So horribly boring.'

'And do they remember me still?'

'Rassilon?' He smiled. 'Oh, yes, they remember him. Though the Rassilon that they remember and honour isn't quite you, you know. He's much more agreeable and saintly.'

I had to laugh at that. 'Sanitized history?'

'Believe me, all of your history is sanitized. It's positively pure, through and through. Still, one or two of us know the truth. And it's not a very nice truth, is it?'

This man is highly dangerous! For all of his

buffoonery and humour, his mind is sharp. He hides his teeth behind an inane smile. 'What are you talking about?'

'Rassilon, Rassilon,' he sighed. 'Don't beat around the bush with me. I know what you are, and what your plans are, because I have seen their results.'

'Perhaps you wouldn't mind enlightening me a little then?'

'Well, we could start with Thremix's little virus, couldn't we? When do you intend to release that?'

Now I knew his source of information, I was considerably happier about talking to him. 'In a few days, probably. Why? Do you disapprove?'

'In some respects, yes. Then there's Omega. What do you intend to do with him?'

His changing of the subject was rather abrupt, but his mind is something like that of a flea – hopping from place to place, never staying still for long. 'I'm not yet sure,' I told him, honestly. 'Why do you ask?'

'If you're thinking of killing him, Rassilon, don't do it. That could be a very serious miscalculation on your part.'

'Kill Omega?' I asked. 'But he's my friend.'

'And, of course, you'd never kill a friend, eh?' He turned very serious. 'Rassilon, you have planned for a long time, I know, but I beg of you, take a while longer. Think about what you are doing, and try to imagine the consequences.'

'Imagine the consequences?' I echoed. 'But why should I do that? You already know the consequences. Why don't you simply tell me about them?'

'My people have a law that forbids our interfering.'

That made me laugh, I can tell you! It was

several minutes before I could stop, and answer him. 'The fact that you are here shows how little respect you hold for that law! Just being here interferes with the course of history. And, I imagine, talking to me like this interferes even more strongly.'

'Not necessarily,' he said. 'You see, I'm supposed to be here. I fit in here, at this moment.'

'And you therefore have a reason for being here,' I told him, flatly. 'I should very much like to know what that reason is.'

'Yes, I rather imagined you would.' He stood up, and crossed to the scanner. Turning it on, he brought up a view across the Panopticon floor. The workmen were still expanding it, and the noise was ferocious, so he turned down the volume. 'I've already seen that room, Rassilon. Every seat filled with pompous jackasses in their regal gowns. Pontificating bureaucrats and venal snakes. What a future you're creating here.'

'But Gallifrey is safe?'

'Safe? Oh, yes, it's safe. It's completely impregnable to everything – especially ideas. Your plans, Rassilon, will create a powerful society that is content to do nothing but sit on its academic qualifications and talk. Gallifrey is so safe, it has isolated itself from change.'

'Perfection does not need change,' I reminded him.

'The Time Lords are not perfect. Far from it. They're inflated with self-importance, they're stuffy beyond endurance, and they are afraid to use their powers for good.'

'Good?' So the man was an idealist. 'And what is good? I'll tell you – whatever makes Gallifrey strong is good. Whatever makes us the masters of all of time and space is good. Anything that advances that day and hour is good.'

'The ends justify the means,' he sighed. 'You don't know how often I've heard that stale, weak philosophy, Rassilon. And it always sickens me. I came here to help you with your schemes, but still hoping to convince you to change the way that the future will be. To make the Time Lords less powerful, less stuck in their ways. To free their grip on the cosmos. To make them able to think again. I can see that that was a mistake on my part. You're far worse than they will ever be.'

'I will not compromise my beliefs,' I told him. 'Whatever the price must be, then I shall pay it. But Gallifrey will be strong. Time Lords – that is what you call the race I am making? A good name! The Lords of Time! That is my desire, my aim.' I studied his tired face again. 'You say you know of me, the real me. Then you know what I have already done. Do you think I could have achieved what I have without this belief in the destiny of Gallifrey? I am willing to risk everything – everything! – to create the very future that you have described.'

'I know,' he agreed. 'You've murdered, schemed and corrupted to get where you are now, and all in the name of idealism. Rassilon, what kind of a society can be based on such a start?'

'My dear fellow, you've already told me – the very future that you have described. One in which Gallifrey is the sole dominant force in time and space, bending even the fabric of the Universe to our wills. Why, the fact that you are here tells me that we shall have that power. It's the culmination of all my dreams, and the end point of all my desires.' I looked him over. 'Just the fact that you are here shows that my plans will succeed. Detonating Polyphilos will work, and we shall have all of the power we shall need to break the constraints of time and space.' Something occurred to me then. 'But if you are here, why haven't I been infected already with the immortality virus?'

'The what?' He looked genuinely perplexed.

'Thremix's little invention.'

'Oh, that.' He grinned again. 'Well, I've got news for you – it's not quite what you hoped of it. It's not a doorway into immortality, you know. It'll increase tremendously the life span of all it touches. And it's going to have a very interesting side effect that Thremix will discover any day now, I believe. But it won't stop death, you know. And it's not as contagious as he thinks. After about a year or so, it will stop infecting people. After that, only those Gallifreyans born with it in their bodies will be able to use it. Not everyone gets it. It's a good job, really. The way I travel, half the Universe would be immortal if it could be passed on.'

'Then my descendants won't all live forever?'

'I've got some more bad news for you, Rassilon: you will never have any descendants at all. You're the last of your line.'

I stared at him, wondering what else he knew that he wasn't telling me. 'And you know all about my future?' I asked him. 'Including how I die?'

'I know something about your future,' he corrected me. 'You and your cohorts and the people who come after you will hide or distort a lot of the truth. And I do not know anything at all about your death. In fact, in my time, there are all kinds of silly children's fables about you. One of them even calls you the Once and Future King, or something along those lines. It says that you never died, and simply sleep on somewhere, to awaken one day and rule Gallifrey once more.' He laughed. 'And there are others that say you were killed in a popular uprising against your incredible tyrannies. Who can say which is true? If either?'

Who indeed? Well, perhaps when we achieve the power to break through the boundaries of space and time I shall be able to discover the answer for myself. After that last pronouncement, he left me to my thoughts, promising he would see me again before he left.

And what thoughts I have had!

He has shown me the future, and it works! Gallifrey has become impregnable. His own fears are simply a result of his misplaced idealism, a disease of the young. When we are strong, then there will be no need to change. We shall have reached that level of grace that Gallifreyans have dreamed of for generations. Perhaps we will not be able to live for ever, but even he admitted that we shall expand our lives many, many times. Why, in two or three normal life spans, what a world I could create! To be able to plan for fifty, a hundred, or a thousand years! To know that anything I envisage can be shaped and built. Ah, what a place this Gallifrey shall become with my hand to guide it down the ages!

DAY 117

Well, one of his predictions has certainly come to pass. Thremix came to see me this morning in an unusually agitated state. When I could get him to calm down and talk to me, he delivered some news that a few short months ago I would have considered to be insane.

He has been conducting more extensive tests of his virus – apparently at *his* urging – and discovered that it possesses a new property that none of us had imagined, but which he, of course, must know: total bodily regeneration.

'At the instant of what should be death,' Thremix explained as best he could, 'the virus restructures the body completely. It remakes it, and allows the new body to begin life afresh.'

'You mean like reincarnation? We start with a clean sheet?'

'Not exactly. We would carry across the process a large amount of our existing memories and personalities. But there would be a great deal of change, I suspect. Features could alter, there could be minor deviations in the psyche, that sort of thing.'

'Then we are indeed talking about true

immortality!' I exclaimed. 'Instead of death, a rebirth! We can all live forever, thanks to you!'

'Not exactly,' he cautioned. 'I've run more tests on the virus itself. It turns out that it isn't anything like as infectious as I had thought. Most people will never be able to inherit it. Those that do will be fully protected, but the rest will never know of it. And some will die because of it. Then, within a year or so, it will stop breeding. After that, its levels will stay constant in the body until regeneration. Then, when the body is restructured, there will be less of the virus left.'

'Which all means?' I demanded.

'Putting it simply,' he sighed, 'about five per cent of the population of Gallifrey is likely to get the virus. Possibly another five per cent will die. The other ninety per cent will be unaffected. The five per cent that is protected by the virus will have extended life spans, and when that span is over, instead of dying, they will be able to regenerate a new body for themselves. They should have sufficient levels of the virus within them to be able to do this probably a dozen times. After that, the level of viral activity will be too low for it to work properly. Then they will die.'

I thought about this for a while. 'Couldn't they simply then be reinfected with the virus? If it worked once, it should work a second time.'

'Think about it,' he said. 'By the time these people have been reborn twelve times, they will not be the same people who started the process. So we'd be back to the same chances again – five per cent of infection, five of death and ninety per cent of nothing at all happening.'

It made sense, but there was one point to consider. 'So there would be a diminishing figure of people who could live beyond that first infection. And of those, there would still be five per cent who could have a third dose...'

'Sooner or later, everyone would die,' he answered. 'Oh, theoretically, someone might always fall into the five per cent forever, but the odds are against it.'

'And how about the children of those people?'

'Again, it's not as good as I had hoped. If the mother is infected with the virus, then she has about a one in ten chance of passing it on to her child. It seems to favour the male for some reason, about two to one.'

I failed to see why he seemed to be so gloomy. 'It sounds to me like you've done excellent work.'

'Hardly that,' was his answer. 'I had hoped to give everyone extended life and health. What the virus will do is to create an elite that will have abilities far above the norm.'

'Come now,' I reasoned. 'There have always been elite groups in history. Society is governed by an elite. All you will be doing is rewarding those people for their work in a very special way.'

'It's easy enough for you to say,' he replied. 'You know that you will be in the elite. How would you feel about the virus if you discovered that it wouldn't work on you?'

'I should not be as happy,' I admitted. 'But for the greater good of Gallifrey, I would be willing to stifle my own pride.'

He sighed. 'Well, I do have one other piece of news about the process. I've been able to refine the virus so that it actually enhances the body when regeneration occurs. Instead of simply rebuilding the body along the original lines, it will improve things somewhat. I've added a double circulatory system, for example. Most deaths occur because of heart failure. With two hearts, there's very little chance of that ever happening. Overall, I think I can say that those who the virus works on will have life spans approaching ten or twelve thousand years. That is, of course, approximate, and dependent on chance, stress and so forth.'

Ten or twelve thousand years! And the idiot was unhappy with what he had done! Well, these geniuses were always a moody lot. And probably the stranger had infected Thremix with some of his idealistic nonsense. There was only one important question left.

'When will the virus be ready for use?'

He frowned again. 'I don't know if we should be using it at all.'

I could hardly believe my ears. 'What are you babbling on about now? Of course we must use it!'

'Haven't you heard a word I've been saying?' he asked. 'If it is released, then we will be creating an elite among our own people. But we will also be murdering just as many innocent people in the process. Is it worth the price?'

I put an arm comfortingly about his shoulders. 'Stop bothering yourself with such questions,' I told him. 'Let me worry about the question of ethics. When can the virus be released?'

'It's ready now,' he replied. 'But I don't know if we should go ahead with it.'

I nodded, sympathetically. 'Well, you simply prepare it for release. Once that is done, we will talk about it some more. If you have any objections, I promise you it will not be released.'

He seemed so pathetically grateful as he hurried off. What a fool. Naturally, I knew he would have no objections to the virus's use.

How could he have? Gimel's man was very careful. He didn't kill Thremix until after the virus was ready for use.

It was a shame that I had to do it, because the man was so brilliant. But I simply could not take the chance that he might have destroyed the virus before it could be used.

DAY 118

A historic day for Gallifrey. It's a pity that my hand is shaking as I write this. Thremix neglected to mention that there would be side effects from the virus. Typical of the man. Still, the medics assure me that the nausea and general lassitude are experienced by all those who have been infected with the virus. The symptoms should pass once our systems get used to the new regime within our bodies.

Thremix was wrong in one other area, too. Initial figures place the successful infections from the virus at almost exactly his five per cent mark, but the death-rate is running closer to ten per cent. At the moment, only about ten or twelve people know the true story of what has happened to Gallifrey, and the planet is in something of a panic. I've had an official cover story made up about an old germ warfare plant having sprung a leak. To make the story more convincing, Gimel has organized an air strike on a site we selected as being useless anyway. Still, with one in ten dying in the streets – some in incredible agony, I have been informed – there is understandably fear abroad. It will calm down soon, when there are no further deaths. The public memory of tragedy especially is very short.

DAY 123

Well, I'm finally back to my old self again – or should that be my new self? I feel wonderful, and have been able to concentrate on matters of state once more. Gimel recovered sooner than I did, and had some interesting reports for me to study.

Naturally, the stranger interrupted me, hopping about in anger, and yelling at me for what I had done. I pointed out, quite rightly, that if I had not had the virus released, then he would not have been alive to come and shout at me. But it made no difference. Fanatics can be quite immune to logic. Then he was off on another tack, trying to get me to stop my other plans, to restructure the Time Lords-to-be into something else. Bored, I began scanning the reports from Gimel, and couldn't stifle my derisory laugh.

'My dear sir, I owe you an apology. I had thought it was because of your pernicious influence that Thremix became reluctant to release his virus. I was quite wrong, it seems.'

'Thremix,' he replied coldly, 'was showing good judgment until he trusted you.'

'His reluctance to release the virus wasn't based on any moral qualms,' I answered. 'It seems that he knew that he was in the ten per cent of the population that would be killed by the virus. Isn't that grimly ironic? If I had not had him killed, he would be dead by his own hand. Would that have been classified as suicide, do you think?'

'Do you think that he would have hesitated for a moment to release the virus if it had meant only his death? It was the other millions that you slaughtered so casually that he was worrying about.'

I was getting very weary of his pretentious prattle. 'Millions of people are simply numbers. He was only afraid for himself. And for that, he would have ruined the fate of the planet! It's a good job that I took the decision out of his hands, isn't it?'

'I don't know why I'm wasting my breath on you,' he sighed. 'You're incapable of grasping any ethical standpoint at all.'

'Don't waste any further breath on my account,' I said, cheerfully.

The next report dealt with Omega. As I had suspected, the man had turned out to be a subversive. He was slinking off to join pro-democratic meetings in secluded corridors of the Capital. It was so primitive, you almost had to feel sorry for them. One of Gimel's men had

infiltrated the group, and we now had the names of all of the ringleaders. Most of them were unimportant, but Omega was far from that.

It left me in a bit of a dilemma. Normally, I would simply have had Gimel round up the troublemakers and quietly dispose of them. But I couldn't afford to lose Omega until we had our temporal control. After that, he became quite expendable. But until he triggered the supernova in the star Polyphilos, I dared not act against the other members of his group. If they should happen to disappear or die, he might turn difficult.

I implemented the obvious solution. Gimel would have them killed once Omega and I led the fleet to Polyphilos. The only thing left now was to ensure that Omega would not return with me.

DAY 140

The final portions of the temporal flux controls are now in place and ready to begin work. They have been installed as close to the Panopticon as I could manage it. Only the few technicians who helped with the work know the exact location of the controller, and they will never pass on their knowledge. I have decided to call the device the Eye of Harmony. In it, all the forces are held in cosmic balance, a true harmony, and from it the power may be tapped to control the Time Drivers.

The technicians working on the TT Capsules have done wonders. I am constantly amazed at the practical applications of pure science. Even though I invented the force barriers and fields that are used in the capsules, what Jelen and her technicians have done with them is truly astounding.

They have sealed each capsule within its own separate field, virtually impregnable once sealed. Entry can be gained only through a key with numerous permutations. The actual lock code will be known only to the operator of the capsules – after all, we should not want any of

them to fall into the wrong hands. Each capsule is to be fed from the Eye of Harmony, and using those chronons and the forces they generate could effectively traverse the known and unknown reaches of time and space.

As if this were not enough, between them they have added several refinements to the plans. This latest capsule is the Type 30, and will feature a chameleon circuit. The capsule's telemetry will scan the area in which it will materialize, and then alter the shape of the enveloping force shield to resemble some native structure in the vicinity. This will enable the capsule, as it materializes, to blend in perfectly with its surroundings. It's a very clever idea, and appeals to me enormously. With the lock and the chameleon device, there is almost no chance at all that any non-Gallifreyan will ever be able to enter a TT Capsule unescorted.

I wonder if it might not be time for the stranger to be permanently retired. I mentioned this thought to Gimel, who – extremely reluctantly – admitted that he had been trying to have him shadowed. It seems that he is always managing either to give the followers the slip or to overpower them somehow. Until now, I had assumed he was simply a nuisance. It seems that he is fast becoming a real problem. I shall have to decide precisely what to do with him shortly.

DAY 162

I suppose I should not have been too surprised, but it seems that the stranger has somehow found out that I intended to have him executed. When Gimel's men broke into his room this morning, he had gone. I have had the Citadel searched, of course, but there is absolutely no sign of him. Obviously he has fled back to wherever he came from, and will no longer be able to harass me.

Omega was furious to discover that he had not only run off, but taken several invaluable items with him. The prototype of the Hand of Omega is missing. This would have been a severe blow to our plans, had not Omega already constructed a second, more sophisticated version of the Hand; we can still proceed with the detonation of Polyphilos.

Along with the missing Hand, some of Omega's 'living metal' has gone also. It's an old device of his he worked on to help defend the planet before I came up with the Transduction Barriers. Since it is no longer really necessary, I don't see its loss as being too serious. Still, I am irked that Gimel's men could allow a stranger to steal anything at all from within the Citadel and then simply to walk off with it. I've given them all standing orders that if he shows up again, he is to be killed on sight. I can't chance his returning for the other Hand before we can use it. Given his idealistic nature, it's not outside the boundaries of possibility that he might do that.

DAY 187

It's almost beyond belief what has happened. Despite my trust and faith in her, Jelen attempted a coup this morning. Now that it is all over, and she and her fellow conspirators are dead, we have begun to piece together what has happened.

Jelen, it seems, took umbrage when the virus killed off her family almost in its entirety. She felt that I was responsible for their murders, and had joined some radical group planning to oust me and to restore the old order. I can't believe that anyone as intelligent as she was could be so utterly foolish as to want back those foolish Councillors. Still, it seems that Pandak and his ilk are a focus for those who do not like my regime. Gimel suggested that it might be better if they were eliminated, but I hesitate to do this. Such a move would suggest that we are afraid of what Pandak and the rest could do, and would be a show of weakness. I favour simply having their contacts watched. Any future conspirators should thus be simple to spot.

Still, Jelen planned well, and was actually equipping her men with portable force shields to enable them to storm the Panopticon and attempt to assassinate me. She had based the shields on the Sash of Rassilon I designed, though, and that was her mistake. I know the weakness of the device, and when Gimel woke me with the news of the revolt, I was soon able to stop it.

Gimel's men could not affect the attacking maniacs, but I could. It was simply a matter of sending a signal that caused the field to contract about each of the wearers. Those that weren't crushed to death were suffocated. Jelen was one of the latter, and I only wish that her death had been more protracted. Such disgusting ingratitude as she showed deserved a far lengthier and more painful demise.

Still, that abortive little revolt shows that there are still some who can plot against me. And that they can find people to take a stance and back them up. It's really quite astonishing – and inevitably foolish. I've allowed Gimel to recruit more agents, and to position them as he deems best.

DAY 203

We are now ready to begin. It's hard to believe, but for the first time in many months, I will be leaving not only the Citadel but also Gallifrey for a short while.

Omega is getting more and more excited as the hour approaches for the fleet to take off. He and I have the smallest craft, and the other eight ships will remain almost a light year from Polyphilos. They will monitor everything that happens, and check that all is going according to plan.

Curious. Had it not been for the stranger, I would probably be in as nervous and excitable a state as Omega is in right now. After all, there is a chance that our tampering with Polyphilos might not power the Eye of Harmony, but in-stead utterly destroy Gallifrey. But I am now certain that this will not happen. Now, I simply wait, knowing that we shall succeed. In two days, Gallifrey will be completely in control of the boundaries of time and space.

And Omega will be dead.

DAY 204

We are now in orbit about Polyphilos. As I write, light from the doomed star illuminates my ship. Hanging here in orbit, it is hard to conceive that tomorrow this entire yellow sun will be no more. Once the forces of the Hand of Omega squeeze it, and the Eye of Harmony locks onto it, then it will explode in a single, intense instant of brightness, and then appear to vanish forever from the Universe. It will be locked within my power.

All is now ready, and I have insisted that everyone in the fleet gets a good night's rest. We do not want any mistakes tomorrow. I know, of course, that we shall succeed – but there is always that little core of doubt within each of us that cries out in fear.

I have consulted with Gimel, in great secrecy. He reports that his men have killed or arrested all of Omega's fellow plotters. What is most ironic is that they had planned to strike against me right after the detonation of Polyphilos. Had Gimel not moved before them, they might even have won. And then control over all of time and space would have been theirs and not —

LATER

The stranger is really most irritating. He interrupted my line of thought, arriving on my ship at the most inopportune moment. I find myself torn between anger and admiration for him. Despite all that I could do to prevent it, he managed to land his TT Capsule on my ship. Clearly the Time Lords that I shall create will

be a most powerful race! And you almost have to admire his gall in daring to arrive just hours before my greatest triumph. I only wish that I could say the same about the asinine speech he came to deliver.

He still has this fanatical determination to try to make me see what he likes to think of as sense. I prefer other words for the liberal drivel that he spouts. I gather he's had something of a strong falling out with the Time Lords of his own era, and now wishes to get his own back at them by erasing them from history. Oh, he never said it in quite those words, of course! Instead, he hides behind a mealy-mouthed rationalization that they have become a stagnant society, introverted and impotent. Clearly, he is interpreting this in his own way. I believe the truth of the matter is that they are a stable, well-ordered society and that they do not change because they have achieved perfection.

When I interrupted his rambling arguments with the accusation that he is simply trying to get back at the regime that has wronged him, he looked most crestfallen. I challenged him to deny that he has been disciplined by them, and his weak defence was that he has been subjected to their whims 'many, many times'.

It is as I suspected all along: the stranger is either dangerously insane, or a criminal. Oh, not a common one, I grant you, but nonetheless a felon. Still, he doesn't lack courage, only intelligence. Perceiving that he was not winning the argument with me, he did finally give up in disgust. Logic isn't one of his better qualities.

'I don't want to prevent your work,' he wheedled. 'Simply to give it a nudge in a different direction.'

'I'm glad to hear that,' I said dryly.

He gave me one of his long stares. 'Don't think that the idea doesn't tempt me,' was his reply. 'You've murdered and enslaved millions of people to get to this point. But the Time Lords are necessary for the future of the Universe, and you are the key to their creation.'

I tried one last time. 'To be able to get to this nexus, I have had no option but to act as I must. Don't think that I enjoy killing anyone. But to achieve stability, those who dig at its roots must be disposed of. I do not kill out of enjoyment, but from necessity. As for enslaving Gallifrey – I think that you'll discover that there is less crime, less poverty and less inequity than ever before.'

'And less freedom,' he retorted.

'Freedom is such an empty word. Freedom to do what? Left to their own devices and imaginations, most people waste their lives. Instead, I have given them a purpose – the elevation of Gallifrey to the strongest power in all of time and space. They have been handed a destiny that changes the entire course of history – are a few lives and the loss of a few freedoms so important that this destiny should be ignored?'

'People have a right to chose the destiny that they want for themselves.'

'Ah, you and Omega would probably get along well! You, too, believe in the outmoded concept of democracy! Let the people decide!' I shook my head. 'The people, left to their own devices, will never decide. And if they do, who is to say that they will make the right choice? Democracy is a foolish system of government.'

'Perhaps so,' he conceded. 'But it's better than any other. Tyranny, for example.'

'Come, am I such a tyrant?' I asked. 'What I do, I do for Gallifrey. If I am a tyrant, then it is with the best of intentions.'

'You're handing to the Time Lords such power as would corrupt a saint, Rassilon,' he responded. 'Even if you were the most pure-hearted tyrant that the Universe has ever known, you cannot guarantee that the same will hold true forever.'

'Perhaps not,' I had to agree. 'But I will do my best to ensure that no tyranny will come from the powers that I endow upon the future members of our race. But I cannot agree with your apocalyptic vision of the future. Make your decision. Go, or stay and watch my new creation.'

Eventually, he left, of course. Not without more and longer speeches, but he finally understood that I stand firm in my resolve. I have not made my choices lightly, and I am not going to change them now. Out of respect for his audacity, I will place safeguards on my spiritual descendants, though. Tyranny of the worse kind can never be tolerated. Only strong rule, and a resolute purpose.

I think that the first Law of Time I shall lay down, though, will be that no Time Lord shall ever travel into his or Gallifrey's own past. The stranger is bad enough with his constant harping on his tired ethics, but suppose that there will come a fanatic one day with similar ideas, but a will to do something positive, such as returning to kill me. No, that cannot ever be allowed.

DAY 205

It is accomplished! We are no longer Gallifreyans, but the Lords of Time!

As I now sit within my offices in the Citadel, the hum of power surrounds me. The Time Control Room is awash with chronons, and the TT Capsules are being prepared for their first real tests. Everything has gone as I desired it. My only partial regret is that I was forced to kill Omega. He would so dearly have loved to be here to see this.

I managed a few, brief hours of sleep, and then awoke to the day of my greatest triumph. Omega and I set the Sashes firmly about us, and I followed his craft into the blazing glory of Polyphilos. There we held our positions, and when the exact moment came, he sent the Hand

of Omega spiralling into the heart of the star.

It was a moment of indescribable beauty. The entire body of the star shook, and ripples of force sped across it. Then, in a brief, burning instant, came the explosion. Without the protection that the Sash afforded me, I should have been annihilated by the flow of radiation that exploded from the dying core.

At the very second that the shields moved to their maximum, closing out the indescribable light that poured from the wreckage of Polyphilos, I used my remote control to shut down Omega's Sash.

His craft disappeared, eradicated in an instant. I am not a harsh man, and am glad that Omega could never have known what happened to him. His body must have been torn apart in a microsecond by the terrible forces that we have unleashed here today.

Back on Gallifrey, the Eye of Harmony captured and chained that outpouring of chronons. The TT circuits within my ship leaped to life, and both I and the fleet were able to leap back to the Citadel in a second. Ah, such a feeling of true exhilaration! To know that the power was finally ours.

Naturally, I made a speech. The Public Access Video spread my words across the entire planet as I broke the news about the tremendous accomplishment that Omega and I had made possible. 'The boundaries of Time and Space have been destroyed,' I proclaimed. 'No longer are we mere Gallifreyans – from this instant on, we are the Lords of Time!'

I also broke the news of the unfortunate death of Omega to them. I invented a story that his force field had failed at the second of explosion, and that sadly he had been destroyed. It would never do for the people to know that he was a traitor, plotting my overthrow. The public has a need of heroes, and dead heroes are so much more convenient than live ones – they are much less likely to stand up and say something

to embarrass you. And you can mould them into whatever shape you chose.

This is the moment of greatest triumph for both myself and for Gallifrey. A new era has begun!

DAY 20,000

I found the old diary that I used to keep the other morning, and read through it. Much of it seems as fresh to my memory as it did then. Some of it I find hard to recall, even on rereading the words. And much has changed since I wrote them.

In the years that have gone by, we Time Lords have consolidated our powers. I have been able to make changes, and there is now a High Council serving me. Naturally, their first move was to elect me President for life. I like a pliable Council.

The Panopticon has been opened up, and the representatives from the various Chapters are now able to take their seats there in debate and on state occasions. The only rule that I have imposed on those holding political powers is that they must be of the new Gallifreyan breed. They must possess the virus that allows them to regenerate.

The stranger, were he here now, would undoubtedly scream and panic, claiming that I have created an elite. Well, he would, I suppose, be correct. We Time Lords are the elite of Gallifrey. Still, given that we have abilities far beyond those of the average person, is it not logical that it should be so? After all, there are thousands of times more insects on Gallifrey than there are people; should we then be required to hand over the planet to their rule? Absurd, of course, as is the notion that the Gallifreyans should be allowed to have a say in the running of Time.

As with all things, change has brought us many problems. I have been more than busy

these last few years simply formulating and imposing the regulations that will govern time travel. As I see I had noted down, I have laid down the First Law that no Time Lord shall ever cross his or her own time lines. I want no revisions of history at this stage.

There has been only one real regret for me since I stopped my diary, and that is the death of Gimel. It is still a hard blow to take, knowing that the one person I had trusted above all should have been planning my overthrow almost from the beginning. However, he did seriously underestimate me, assuming that I had allowed him to set up his little net of spies unsupervised. My own agents within his little clique gave me timely warnings of his intentions. His miniature revolution was nipped in the bud, and he was able to perform one last task for our race by dying.

It's odd, but before his conspiracy, it had never occurred to me that it might become necessary one day to execute a Time Lord. It took a little imagination on our part to accomplish it, of course. After all, the usual staser shot to the head would hardly work, given Gimel's powers of regeneration. Instead, one of my aides came up with the concept of vaporization. When we tried it, it worked beautifully – every single particle in the victim's body is disassembled, and scattered into the Vortex of Time and Space. There is no chance at all of bodily regeneration. I have now had it written into the Codes that any Time Lords that must be executed should be disposed of in this manner.

It is sad, though, that Gimel's death should have become so inevitable. Thremix, Omega, Jelen . . . all of the people who began this grand design with me are now dead. And our foes, too, Pandak and Mayeron. I sometimes wonder why death is always such a prelude to change, but it seems to inevitably be so.

Well, for now, this is enough. I believe that my diary is complete, and I shall seal it – and the secrets it contains – away. Perhaps some day it will be recovered, and read. Perhaps not. It hardly seems to matter. Still, I do not wish to finish this narrative on a depressing note, and should perhaps explain why I no longer need to keep this written record.

One of the brighter of the younger Time Lords has invented what he calls an Exitonic Circuit. It appears to be basically a net of artificial brain cells that constantly update the information that they carry. He tells me that this Amplified Panatropic Net of his will be able to record the mental processes and thoughts of any person. I can see that it will have many uses, perhaps even more than now seems possible. But from this point on, I shall certainly use it to store information that before I have only dared to write down.

Again, I find my memory returning to that impudent interloper. His prediction that the Time Lords would become brooding, introspective failures seems to be no more than his own dissatisfaction written on to the whole race. The Time Lords are a bright, alert species, and we are constantly expanding our horizons. Already we have conquered the boundaries of Time and Space. We have shaken the grim hold that death has always held over us. We can now record emotions, thoughts and memories forever. All this in so short a period of time! Given the vast frontiers that are now open to us, who can say what the Time Lords may not some day be able to accomplish?

FINAL ENTRY

Rassilon is now finished, and it has fallen to my task either to seal or destroy all of his records. Accordingly, I have searched through his offices, and come upon this box of scrolls. It has apparently lain here for many centuries, all but forgotten even by Rassilon himself. I sat, quite engrossed, in reading his accounts of the formation of the society we now have.

He has ruled a long time – almost a thousand years – and much has happened since he wrote. Still, it is not my place to attempt to chronicle those events. I am simply ending his narrative with a few notes on what has happened to him. Then these scrolls shall be sealed. I will recommend that they never be opened. Already, in just a few years, Rassilon has become something of a legend among the common people of Gallifrey. How quickly the general populace seems to forget his darker side. But perhaps that is to the good. As Rassilon himself remarked, heroes are often needed, and dead heroes are the best of all.

Not that he is dead, exactly. I had voted for termination, but the general assembly overruled this. Partly this was due to a fear that Rassilon had somehow set a trap in the vaporization booth that would not kill him, but simply transport him somewhere. It's hard to argue with this opinion – after all, he was an accomplished engineer, and possessed a feverishly devious mind. The other part of the reluctance to kill him stemmed from the fact that the new regime did not wish to begin as Rassilon himself had, with executions and repressions.

In the end, they elected merely for eternal imprisonment. He was taken and confined by force screens – ones he did not himself design! – within the Dark Tower at the heart of the Forbidden Zone. His body would remain immobile as long as the screens last – which will be while the Eye of Harmony can drain any power at all from the outer cosmos. If Rassilon does ever waken, then it will be as the ruler of a dead and barren world.

Curiously, he did not seem at all dismayed by the sentence imposed upon him. He looked upon it as a step into immortality. Reading back through the records he has left, I am forced to wonder how honest his thoughts contained in these scrolls have been. Is he merely another Time Lord – perhaps the greatest of us, but still similar? Or did Thremix design a second, better virus for his own use? The original virus, Rassilon notes, would have killed Thremix. I find myself wondering if the brilliant biologist then worked on a second strain, one that might have granted him full immortality . . . And with

Thremix's death, did Rassilon then appropriate this virus for his own use?

Such speculations are fruitless. Rassilon will never again talk. I am almost certain that it is merely my own fears speaking in the night to me. But there are hints within Rassilon's records that he is not the same kind of being as we are. His earlier writings, for example, show his worries about selecting a successor to himself. Towards the end, this thought has vanished. Is this simply because he felt he had a longer time in which to make his decision? Or did he believe himself to be truly immortal, and thus in no need at all to determine his successor?

Anyway, I have spoken to no one of my worries. It would surely do no good at all to share these fears. And I will have these scrolls sealed away. Perhaps if I were a braver person I would simply burn them, but they contain such valuable material that I find myself hesitating. One day, perhaps, a wiser, kinder society may evolve, and the truths locked within these scrolls – along with the distortions of that truth that infects all that Rassilon writes – may be made known.

Enough. I have finished, and to this final page, I fix my seal.

Pandak III

Under this entry, one final word has been written. The handwriting, of a much later date, belongs to ex-President Borusa. It reads, simply:

Interesting.

APPENDIX II:
THE
CAST LIST

THE DOCTOR

(1) William Hartnell
(2) Patrick Troughton
(3) Jon Pertwee
(4) Tom Baker
(5) Peter Davison
(6) Colin Baker
(7) Sylvester McCoy

SUSAN

Carole Ann Ford

ROMANA

(1) Mary Tamm
(2) Lalla Ward

RASSILON

Richard Mathews

OMEGA

(1) Stephen Thorne
(2) Ian Collier

THE MONK

Peter Butterworth

THE MASTER

(1) Roger Delgado
(2) Peter Pratt
(3) Geoffrey Beevers
(4) Anthony Ainley

BORUSA

(1) Angus MacKay
(2) John Arnatt
(3) Leonard Sachs
(4) Philip Latham

THE RANI

Kate O'Mara

THE VALEYARD

Michael Jayston

THE RENEGADES

Edward Brayshaw – The War Chief
Kevin Lindsay – Cho-Je
George Cormack – K'Anpo
Michael Spice – voice of Morbius
Stuart Fell – Morbius
Barry Jackson – Drax
Maurice Denham – Azmael

OTHER TIME LORDS

The War Games
Bernard Horsfall
Trevor Martin
Clyde Pollitt

Terror of the Autons
David Garth

Genesis of the Daleks
John Franklyn-Roberts

The Deadly Assassin
Llewellyn Rees (President)
Bernard Horsfall (Goth)
George Pravda
(Castellan Spandrell)
Derek Seaton
(Commander Hildred)
Eric Chitty (Engin)
Hugh Walters (Runcible)
Maurice Quick (Gold Usher)
Peter Mayock (Solis)
John Dawson
Micheal Bilton
(Time Lords)

Colony in Space
Peter Forbes-Robertson
John Baker
Graham Leaman

The Three Doctors
Graham Leaman
Tony Lang
Lincoln Wright
Richard Orme
Peter Evans
Clyde Pollitt (Chancellor)
Roy Purcell (President)

The Invasion of Time
Milton Johns
(Castellan Kelner)
Christopher Tranchell
(Andred)
Dennis Edwards (Gomer)
Reginald Jessup (Savar)
Charles Morgan (Gold Usher)
Hilary Ryan (Rodan)
Max Faulkner (Nesbin)
Ray Callaghan (Ablif)

Gai Smith (Presta)
Michael Mundell (Jasko)
Christopher Christou
Michael Harley
Eric Danot
(Chancellery Guards)

Arc of Infinity
Michael Gough (Hedin)
Colin Baker (Maxil)
Paul Jerricho (Castellan)
Neil Daglish (Damon)
Elspeth Gray (Thalia)
Max Harvey (Zorac)
John D. Collins (Talor)

The Five Doctors
Dinah Sheridan
(Chancellor Flavia)
Stephen Meredith
(Technician)
Stuart Blake (Commander)
Paul Jerricho (Castellan)
Johnnie Mack
Frederick Wolfe
Charles Milward
(Time Lords)

The Ultimate Foe
James Bree
(The Keeper of the Matrix)

THE GUARDIANS

Cyril Luckham
(White Guardian)
Valentine Dyall
(Black Guardian)